INSIDE
STORIES
I

was made a peer of France and General of the Royal Guard. In 1830 he opposed Louis Philippe and went into exile with Charles X. He finally settled in Vienna and became tutor to Napoleon's son. He died in Venice in March 1852.

⁴ *The Comte d'Artois*, subsequently Charles X, and known as Monsieur, was the brother and successor of Louis XVIII. Born in 1757 he escaped from France in 1789 and sought asylum in Holyrood Palace, Edinburgh. On the restoration of his brother he headed the reactionary party of the ultra-royalists and on succeeding to the throne behaved with such narrow stupidity that he was mainly responsible for the Revolution of July 1830. He then retired again to Holyrood and died at Goritz in 1836. "The Comte d'Artois," wrote Lady Holland, "is a man of slender abilities with violent passions; before the Revolution he was weak and volatile; he is now weak and revengeful."

⁵ The first and conditional abdication in favour of the King of Rome ran as follows: "The Allied Powers having proclaimed that the Emperor Napoleon was the sole obstacle to the re-establishment of peace in Europe, the Emperor Napoleon declares that he is ready to abandon the throne, to leave France and even to sacrifice his life" in favour of his son, the King of Rome. The second and unconditional abdication, after a similar preamble, continued: "The Emperor Napoleon, remaining faithful to his oath, declares that he renounces for himself and his heirs the thrones of France and Italy and that there is no personal sacrifice, even that of his life, that he would not be ready to make in the interests of France. . . ."

It is curious to note that the first abdication, that of April 4, was dated from "*our* palace of Fontainebleau," whereas the second, that of April 11, is dated from "*the* palace of Fontainebleau."

⁶ From 1808 onwards Napoleon had worn round his neck a small heart-shaped satchel containing a poison prepared according to a formula given by Cabanis to Condorcet. In 1812 he substituted for this a prescription prepared for him by Dr. Yvan; it was this dose which failed him in 1814. In 1815 he carried with him, attached to his braces, a far more potent poison; he did not use this after Waterloo on the ground that he "must fulfil his destiny."

IDE
RIES
I

ed by

/ Richard Davies

RCOURT
BRACE
CANADA

e & Company, Canada
San Diego • London • Sydney

Canadian Cataloguing in Publication Data

Main entry under title:

Inside stories 1

For secondary school students.
ISBN 0-7747-1271-6

1. Short stories, Canadian (English).⋆   2. Short stories, American.   3. Short stories, English.
I. Kirkland, Glen.   II. Davies, Richard.

PN6120.2.I58 1987   823′.01′08   C87-093769-3

ISBN 0-7747-1271-6

94 95 BBM 9 8

Cover: "Rock in the Woods" by Tom Forrestall C.M. R.C.A. is reproduced by permission of the artist.

Text and cover design: Michael van Elsen Design Inc.
Composition: CompuScreen Typesetting Ltd.
Printed and bound in Canada by Best Book Manufacturers Inc.

R 7

17). Born at Mereczowszczyno.
n Germany, Italy and France.
of the American Colonies as a
at Yorktown. Accorded rank of
United States citizenship. Re-
ught to enlist sympathy of the
. In 1793 invited by Polish insur-
3, 1794, he defeated the Russians
armies were annihilated and he
er. He was released and returned
ed till 1798. He refused to join
e at Berville near Fontainebleau.
lothurn where he died on April 2,

ré") (1755-1824). Third son of
KV, and Maria Josepha of Saxony.
XVI he was regarded as the heir to
ieur. At the time of the flight to
vith his favourite, Count d'Avaray,
ped to Hamm in Westphalia from
to Brunswick and then to Mittau
from Mittau he spent three years
k final refuge in England, first at
rl of Buckingham, and finally at
longing to Sir George Lee.

PTER 8

er virtues, was a stupid woman; she
t became stout in middle age. Lady
t of her which is so vivid and so
be recorded: "No one was ever so
he sometimes provokes me; there is a
he cares of life in her round grey eye
ever felt any crosses or knows the
She talks with equal indifference of
, the Baby and the Furniture, the

To the many students
who enjoy writing and reading
short stories

G.K.

R.D.

TABLE OF CONTENTS

ACKNOWLEDGMENTS

The authors give special acknowledgment to the Edmonton Catholic and Public School Boards for their support.

The authors and publisher gratefully acknowledge the teacher-reviewers and student-reviewers listed below for their contribution to the development of this program:

Joy Alpert
English teacher, Humber College, Toronto, Ontario

Brian Penman
Head of English Department, Oakville Trafalgar High School, Oakville, Ontario

Stefan Sierakowski
Associate Head of English Department, Lester B. Pearson Collegiate Institute, Scarborough, Ontario

Douglas Van Hamme
Head of English Department, Dr. Norman Bethune Collegiate Institute, Scarborough, Ontario

Students at Bloor Collegiate, Summer School, 1986, Toronto, Ontario

Students at Humberside Collegiate Institute, 1986, Toronto, Ontario

TO THE STUDENT

Welcome to *Inside Stories*. This book contains twenty-four stories, a blend of the modern and the classic. As well as stories by such recognized writers as Morley Callaghan, Alice Munro, Jane Rule, Ray Bradbury, and Saki, we have included selections by more recently established and emerging writers such as Maara Haas and Mary Peterson.

We have attempted to expose you to a wide cross-section of subjects and themes and a well-balanced representation of male and female protagonists. Through these stories you will travel to other places and times, encountering both the strange and the familiar, and meeting some remarkable human beings. We hope there is something here for everyone.

The book is organized into six units according to various elements of fiction, followed by a seventh unit that invites you to read beyond the focuses of the initial units. Each section begins with a brief commentary that introduces a particular focus and invites you to read the stories. Immediately after each story are follow-up questions that ask you to consider the work's special qualities and to share some of your own views and experiences.

Difficult vocabulary and allusions, as well as background information on the authors, have been placed in a separate section at the back of the book (page 241). There, too, you will find a glossary of the most common terms for reference during the study of the short story (page 254).

The truly valuable aspect of this book lies in the connections you will make between the selections and your own thoughts, feelings, and experiences as you "get inside" each story. We will not delay you any longer—except to wish you happy reading.

G.K.
R.D.

1 THE STORY EXPERIENCE

Ever since the first cave dweller came back from the hunt and recounted its events to his companions, human beings have been fascinated by stories. We can remember times when somebody read a story to us or told us a story. Now we still look for and enjoy stories, mostly in the form of books, magazines, movies, and television shows. Sometimes, though, we will find a story in other places, such as a friend's phone call, a song, or a letter. What fascination do stories have that keeps us interested in reading or hearing more of them?

We have only to remember those times when our imaginations were swept away by a story to know their first appeal lies in their value as entertainment. We enjoy being taken into the lives and conflicts of others, into adventures beyond our personal experiences, and into new places and worlds vastly different from the ones we know.

In addition to their value as entertainment, stories have a second appeal that usually fascinates readers. They tell us about the lives of the story's characters, allowing us to become well acquainted with another individual's innermost thoughts and feelings. As that character responds to conflicts or needs, we come to understand his or her motivation and approach to life. This understanding can sometimes give us greater insight into ourselves, others in our lives, and our society.

The selections in this unit illustrate the range and depth of appeal stories can have. The first story, "The Friday Everything Changed," describes a conflict that leads to important insights into traditions. The second story, "Wish You Were Here," is mostly entertaining; readers are intrigued by the mysterious events and shocked by the final revelation. The third story, "The Whale," is a light-hearted romantic tale with a twist. Each selection is a unique reading experience that will reacquaint readers with the value of stories.

Anne Hart

THE FRIDAY EVERYTHING CHANGED

Tradition. In Miss Ralston's class the boys have always carried the water bucket. Until one day, the girls decide it's time to challenge the rule . . .

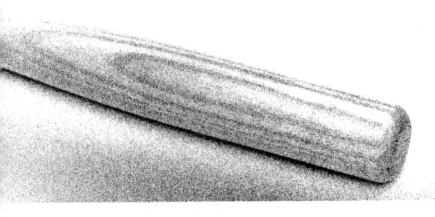

The last hour of school on Friday afternoons was for Junior Red Cross. The little kids would get out their Junior Red Cross pins and put them on and us big kids would start elbowing down the aisles to the book cupboard at the back to see who would get the interesting magazines. There was a big pile of them and they were of two kinds: the *National Geographic* and the *Junior Red Cross News*. Because the boys were stronger and sat near the back they usually got the *National Geographics* first, which meant they could spend the rest of Red Cross looking at African ladies wearing nothing on top, while us girls had to be satisfied with the *Junior Red Cross News*, which showed little African kids wearing lots of clothes and learning how to read. Apart from the magazines for the big kids and maybe the teacher reading a story to the little kids, about the only other thing that happened regularly during Red Cross was picking the two boys who would carry water the next week.

In our school the water bucket always stood on a shelf at the front of the room just behind the teacher's desk. First you'd make a paper cup out of a piece of scribbler paper, then you'd grab the teacher's attention from wherever it happened to be and then up you'd go to the front of the room for a drink from the water bucket.

It was kind of interesting to stand at the front of the room behind the teacher's desk and drink water. The school looked different from up there and sometimes you could get just a glimpse of an idea of what the teacher thought she was all about. I mean, from the front, looking down on those rows of kids with their heads bent over their desks and the sun coming in the windows and the blackboards and all that stuff on the walls, you might almost think, at first glance, that you were looking at one of those real city schools —like in the health books—where the kids were all so neat and all the same size. But after the first strange moment it just became our school again, because you had to start adding in things like the coal stove and the scarred old double desks and the kids themselves. I mean, we just didn't look like the kids in those pictures. Maybe it was because we were so many different sizes—from the kids snuffling in the front rows over their Nan and Dan readers to the big boys hunched over their desks at the back—maybe it was because we wore so many heavy clothes all the time, or maybe it was because of something that wasn't even there at all but seemed to be on the faces of the kids in those city pictures: a look as if they liked being where they were.

But all that's a long way from Junior Red Cross and who would carry the water.

The water for our school came from a pump at the railway station, which was about a quarter of a mile away. One day long ago a health inspector had come around and had announced that water must be made available to the school. For a while there had been some talk of digging a well but in the end we got a big, shiny, galvanized water bucket and permission to use the railway station pump. And from that day on—for all the boys—the most important thing that happened at school, even more important than softball, was who would get to carry the water.

If you were a boy it was something you started dreaming about in Grade 1, even though there was not the remotest chance it could ever happen to you before at least Grade 5, and only then if the teacher thought you were big and strong enough. You dreamed about it partly because carrying the water meant you were one of the big guys, and carrying the water meant you could get away from school for maybe half an hour at a time. But mostly you dreamed about it because carrying the water was something real, and had absolutely nothing whatever to do with Nan and Dan and all that stuff.

So every Friday afternoon toward the end of Red Cross, when it got to be time for the teacher to pick the two boys who would go for water the next week, all the *National Geographics* came to rest like huge butterflies folding up their yellow wings and a big hush fell all over the back rows. And that's the way it had always been until one extraordinary afternoon when, right out of the blue, just after the teacher had picked Ernie Chapman and Garnet Dixon to carry the water, my seatmate, Alma Niles, put up her hand and said: "Why can't girls go for the water, too?"

If one of those German planes, like in the war movies, had suddenly appeared over the school and dropped a bomb, we all couldn't have been more surprised. A silence fell over the room and in that silence everyone looked at the teacher.

Now our teacher that year was named Miss Ralston and even though she came from River Hibbert we all liked her quite a lot. She was strict but she was never really mean like some of the teachers we'd had. Because she was young (she'd just finished Grade 11 the year before herself—River Hibbert had fancy things like Grade 11) she'd had quite a rough time the first week of school with the bigger boys. But she was pretty big herself and after she'd strapped most of them up at the front of the room before our very eyes (and even the little kids could see that it really hurt) things had settled down. The boys kind of admired Miss Ralston for strapping so hard, and us girls admired her because she was so pretty and wore nylon stockings and loafers all the time. But the really unusual thing about Miss Ralston was the way she sometimes stopped in the middle of a lesson and looked at us as if we were real people, instead of just a lot of kids who had to be pushed through to their next grades. And that was why, on that Friday afternoon when Alma

5

Niles put up her hand and said: "Why can't girls go for the water, too?" we all turned and looked at Miss Ralston first instead of just bursting out laughing at Alma right away.

And Miss Ralston, instead of saying, "Whoever heard of girls going for the water?" or, "Are you trying to be saucy, Alma?" like any other teacher would, said nothing at all for a moment but just looked very hard at Alma, who had gone quite white with the shock of dropping such a bombshell. After a long moment, when she finally spoke, Miss Ralston, instead of saying, "Why that's out of the question, Alma," threw a bombshell of her own: "I'll think about that," she said—as if, you know, she *would*—"and I'll let you know next Friday."

The trouble started right away as soon as we got into the schoolyard, because all the boys knew, from the moment Miss Ralston had spoken, that something of theirs was being threatened and that, as long as there was the remotest chance that any girl might get to carry the water, they had to do everything in their power to stop it. Like driving a tractor or playing hockey for the Toronto Maple Leafs, carrying water was real, and because it was real it belonged to them.

So they went right for Alma as soon as she came out of school and that was when another funny thing happened. Instead of just standing back and watching Alma get beaten up, as we usually did when the boys were after someone, the girls rushed right in to try and help her. In the first place we all liked Alma, and in the second place we all had seen, as clearly as the boys, what our carrying the water might mean; that, incredibly, we, too, might get to skip school for half an hour at a time, that we, too, might get to sneak into Rowsell's store on the way back and, most dizzying thought of all, that we too might get to do something real.

And, because we were so intoxicated by the whole idea, and took the boys so much by surprise by standing up to them, we somehow managed to get Alma and ourselves out of the schoolyard with only a few bruises and torn stockings, leaving the boys in possession of the schoolyard where, as we could glimpse over our shoulders as we ran down the hill, they had begun to gather together in a single ominous knot.

And for the rest of that weekend, though of course we never talked about it in front of our parents, all we could think of, both boys and girls, was what was going to happen at school that coming week.

The first thing, clearly evident by recess on Monday morning, was that the boys had decided not to let us girls field at softball any more.

Softball at our school used to go like this: every Monday morning at recess two of the bigger boys—that year it was usually Ernie Chapman and Junior LeBlanc—used to pick their teams for the week. Whoever came out on top in laddering hands up the softball bat got to pick first and the loser second and so it went—back and forth—until all the boys who were considered good enough to be on a team had been picked. Then Ernie and Junior laddered the bat again to see which side would get up first and the losing side took to the field to be joined by the little boys who hadn't been picked and us older girls who were allowed to act as sort of permanent supplementary fielders. And for the rest of the week the teams remained locked, at every recess and lunchtime, in one long softball game which had, as we discovered to our surprise several years later when the television came through, some strange rules.

The way we played, for example, every single boy had to get out before the other team could come in. And any boy hitting a home run not only had the right to bat straight away again but also to bring back into the game any boy who had got out. Which led to kids who couldn't remember their six-times table properly being able to announce—say, by noon on Thursday—"The score's now 46 to 39 because, in the last inning starting Tuesday lunchtime, Junior's team was all out except for Irving Snell, who hit three homers in a row off of Lorne Ripley, and brought in Ira and Jim and Elton who brought in the rest except for Austin who got out for the second time on Wednesday with a foul ball one of the girls caught behind third base . . ."

Some days it got so exciting that at noon we couldn't wait to eat our lunches but would rush straight into the schoolyard, gobbling our sandwiches as we ran, toward that aching moment when the ball, snaking across the yellow grass or arching toward us from the marsh sky, might meet our open, eager hands.

So it was a hard blow, Monday morning recess, when Ernie Chapman whirled the bat around his head, slammed it down as hard as he could on home base and announced. "The first girl that goes out to field, *we break her neck*." We clustered forlornly around the girls' entry door knowing there was nothing we could really do.

"Oh Alma," mourned Minnie Halliday, biting the ends of her long, brown braids, "why couldn't you just have kept your mouth shut?" It was a bad moment. If we'd tried to go out to field they'd have picked us off one by one. We couldn't even play softball on our own. None of us owned a bat and ball.

If it hadn't been for Doris Pomeroy, we might have broken rank right there and then. Doris, who was in Grade 9 and had had a home permanent and sometimes wore nail polish and had even, it was rumored, gone swimming in the quarry all alone with Elton Lawrence, flicked a rock against the schoolhouse wall in the silence following Minnie's remark and steadied us all by saying: "Don't be foolish, Minnie. All we have to do is wait. They need us to field and, besides, they kind of like to have us out there looking at them when they get up to bat."

But it was a long, hard week. Besides not letting us field, the boys picked on us whenever they got the chance. I guess they figured that if they made things bad enough for us, sooner or later we'd go to Miss Ralston and ask her to forget the whole thing. But all their picking on and bullying did was to keep us together. Whenever one of us was tripped going down the aisle or got an ink ball in her hair or got trapped in the outhouse by a bunch of boys it was as if it was happening to all of us. And looking back on that week—when there were so many bad feelings and so many new feelings in the air—it was kind of nice, too, because for the first time us girls found ourselves telling each other our troubles and even our thoughts without worrying about being laughed at. And that was something new at our school.

As for Alma, who kept getting notes thrown on her desk promising her everything from a bloody nose to having her pants pulled down, we stuck to her like burrs. But maybe Alma's hardest moment had nothing to do with bullying at all. It was when her cousin Arnold came over to see her Wednesday after school and asked her to drop the whole idea of girls going for the water.

"If they find out about it, Alma," said Arnold. "they'll probably take away the water bucket."

"Who's they?" asked Alma. She and Arnold had played a lot

together when they were little kids and she was used to listening to his opinions on most things.

"Well, the health inspector," said Arnold, "and guys like that."

"They'll never take away that water bucket," said Alma, though she wasn't all that sure. "They don't care who carries the water as long as it gets carried."

"Alma," said Arnold earnestly, "the other guys would kill me if they ever found out I told you this but sometimes carrying the water isn't that much fun. On cold days it's real hard work. You're better off in the warm school."

Alma knew what it cost Arnold to tell her this but she stood firm. "I'm sorry, Arnold," she said. "but I'm used to cold weather. In winter I walk to school the same as you." So Arnold went away.

If Miss Ralston, as the week wore on, noticed anything unusual going on in her school, she gave little sign of it. She passed out the usual punishments for ink balls, she intercepted threatening notes and tore them up unread, she looked at Alma's white face, and all she asked about were the principal rivers of Europe. Nor were we surprised. Nothing in our experience had led us to believe the grown-ups had the slightest inkling—or interest—in what really went on with kids.

Only Doris Pomeroy thought differently. "Miss Ralston looks real mad," said Doris as we trailed in thankfully from Friday morning recess.

"Mad?" a couple of us asked.

"Yeah. Like when she comes out to ring the bell and we're all hanging around the entry door like a lot of scared chickens. She rings that old handbell as if she wished all those yelling boy's heads were under it. Of course they do things differently in River Hibbert. I know for a fact that girls there get to play on softball teams just like the boys."

"On teams? Just like the boys?" But it was all too much for us to take in at that moment, so preoccupied were we with that afternoon's decision on the water. All that long, hard week it was as if Friday afternoon and Junior Red Cross would never come again. Now that it was almost upon us most of us forgot, in our excitement, at least for the time being, Doris' heady remark about softball.

So at lunchtime, just as the boys were winding up their week's game ("And real great, eh? Without the girls?" Ernie Chapman was gloating loudly from the pitcher's mound), when Miss Ralston, without her bell, leaped through our clustered huddles at the entry door and headed straight toward the softball field, she took us all completely by surprise. Crunch, crunch, crunch went Miss Ralston's bright red loafers against the cinders and the next thing we knew she'd grabbed the bat from Irving Snell and, squinting against the sun, was twirling and lining it before our astonished eyes.

"Come on! Come on!" cried Miss Ralston impatiently to Ernie who stood transfixed before her on the pitcher's mound. "Come on! Come on!" she cried again and she banged the bat against the ground.

"Come on! Come on!" cried Doris Pomeroy and we rushed after her across the cinders.

The first ball Ernie threw was pretty wobbly and Miss Ralston hit it at an angle so that it fell sideways, a foul ball, toward George Fowler's outstretched hands. "Ah-h-h-h-h," we moaned from the sidelines and some of us closed our eyes so we wouldn't have to look. But George jumped too eagerly for such an easy ball and it fell right through his fingers and rolled harmlessly along the ground.

Ernie took a lot more time over his second pitch. He was getting over the first shock of finding Miss Ralston opposite him at bat and by this time he was receiving shouts of encouragement from all over the field.

"Get her! Get her!" the boys yelled recklessly at Ernie and they all fanned out behind the bases.

Ernie took aim slowly. None of us had ever seen the pirouettings of professional pitchers but there was a certain awesome ceremony, nevertheless, as Ernie spat savagely on the ball, glared hard at Miss Ralston, slowly swung back his big right arm and, poised for one long moment, his whole body outstretched, threw the ball as hard as he could toward home base where Miss Ralston waited, her body rocking with the bat.

For a fleeting moment we had a glimpse of what life might be like in River Hibbert and then Miss Ralston hit the ball.

"Ah-h-h-h-h-h," we cried as it rose high in the air, borne by the marsh wind, and flew like a bird against the sun, across the road and out of sight, into the ox pasture on the other side.

"Ah-h-h-h-h-h . . ."

We all stared at Miss Ralston. "School's in," she announced over her shoulder, walking away. Hitting the ball into the ox pasture happened maybe once a year.

That afternoon, toward the end of Red Cross, there was a big hush all over the room.

"Next week," said Miss Ralston, closing the school register, tidying her books, "next week Alma Niles and Joyce Shipley will go for the water."

She swept her hand over the top of her desk and tiny dust motes danced in the slanting sun.

Responding

1. Why are the boys so upset at the idea of the girls carrying the water bucket?

2. What strategies do the boys use to pressure the girls to give in? How do the girls react?

3. At one point in the story, Doris Pomeroy comments that their teacher looks very angry. What do you suppose Miss Ralston thinks of what is taking place?

4. What point does Miss Ralston make when she hits the home run? Why does no one protest when she announces that Alma and Joyce will go for water next Friday?

5. What qualities make this story entertaining? Does it have, as well, a significant message for readers to consider? Explain.

6. Write a diary entry that Miss Ralston might have written the night before she revealed her decision.

7. Improvise a conversation in which three or four students and Miss Ralston recall the incident at a reunion ten years later.

Student notes, page 241

Frank Jones

WISH YOU WERE HERE

Lawn ornaments are not capable of writing postcards from faraway places.
Or are they?

They were walking towards the car when Dorothy noticed him. "Isn't he darling, Norah," she said, stopping and pointing. On the way home from Norah's cottage they had made their usual stop at the doughnut shop and, coming out, Dorothy's eye had been caught by an object in the garden centre next door.

"Kinda cute," her friend agreed. "If you like that sort of thing."

"But I do," said Dorothy. "And I know exactly the place for him. You know that spot alongside the irises in the rockery—sort of an arbor?"

Norah nodded.

"Well, can't you just see him perched there? Come on, Norah. Let's see how much they want."

The sign said "Van Houten", and it wasn't hard to place the ruddy-faced man taking off his leather gloves as a Dutchman. "Can I help you ladies?" The rolling L-sound was a dead giveaway.

"I was interested in that gnome," said Dorothy. "How much are you asking?"

"He's a cute little rascal, isn't he," said the nurseryman. "Well, he's marked at twenty-five dollars." He seemed to be thinking. "Look, I'll tell you what happened. I sold him once already, but the people brought him back for credit. Didn't suit their garden, I guess. I'll let you have him for twenty dollars."

"Do you really want it?" Norah asked in an undertone. "Don't you think it's a bit, well, corny?"

Dorothy walked around the gnome, admiring the red and white toadstool on which he sat and the mischievous expression on his face. "Yes," she said at last. "Yes, I really want him. Norah, you don't mind, do you, if we put him in the trunk? Will you put him in the back of the car for us?" she asked the nurseryman.

When they got to Dorothy's place, Norah went to give her a hand lifting the gnome. "Wait, I'll get the wheelbarrow. He's heavier than I thought," said Dorothy. They trundled him across the lawn and then, bracing their feet against the rocks, lifted him into position.

"Doesn't he look just perfect there?" Dorothy bubbled. "As if the spot had just been waiting for him."

"Not bad," said Norah.

"Ted, when he was alive, never liked ornamental things in the garden, but now there's only myself to please. No," she said, putting her hand on Norah's arm, "I'll put the wheelbarrow away later. Come inside and I'll put the kettle on for tea."

When Norah had gone home, Dorothy went out again and swivelled the gnome until his lop-sided grin was directed towards the living-room picture window. "There, Mr. Gnome, now I'll be able to enjoy you winter and summer." she said. The gnome, one eye half-closed in the beginnings of a wink, seemed to be agreeing with her.

"He sure looks cute, Mrs. Graham." She gave a start and turned around. It was only Norman, the mailman, standing there with his empty bag, but she felt her cheeks flush at the thought that he might have heard her talking to herself.

"Just puts a nice finishing touch to the garden," he said, flicking back the lick of hair that always got behind his glasses. Norman was only in his mid-twenties, but he took an almost fatherly interest in the older people on his route. If he didn't see one of his customers for a couple of days, he'd make a point of knocking to make sure everything was all right.

"That's just what I thought," said Dorothy gratefully. "The spot seems made for him."

She had her housecoat on and was having breakfast in the kitchen next morning when the doorbell rang. Through the window at the side door she could see it was Norman, and she wondered idly who would be sending her a registered letter this time of year.

"Morning, Mrs. Graham," he said. "Thought I better tell you—them kids have been up to mischief again. Look what they did to your dwarf."

"Gnome, Norman," she said, stepping out onto the porch. The gnome had been tipped from his perch and was lying face-down among the sweet william.

"I'll put it up again for you," he said, resting his bag on the steps. "Maybe it was those Allen boys." He and Dorothy had talked before about the random incidents of petty vandalism that seemed to plague the neighborhood in cycles. "For sale" signs would be pulled up in the night and stuck in front of other houses, lawn chairs would be tipped over, and flowerbeds trampled. Dorothy realized it wasn't fair to blame the Allen boys, but sometimes when they went down the street shouting obscenities with their friends and hitting every road sign they passed, it was hard to believe they were not behind the mischief.

"Well, thank you, Norman. It was very kind of you," she said as he picked up his bag after righting the gnome.

After breakfast she took a damp cloth out to the garden and wiped away the earth staining the gnome's face. "There you are, old fellow," she said. "Feel better now?" He smiled his slightly conspiratorial smile.

For a couple of days nothing more happened. Then one morning when she went to the window she was surprised to see that he had been pushed over again. "This is too much!" she said furiously. "Too much! I'm going to put a stop to it right now."

She put on her shoes and, not even bothering to lift the gnome up again, strode up the street to the slightly run-down bungalow where the Allens lived. Old yellowed newspapers clung to the fence and a tired-looking dog rolled off the step and sniffed Dorothy's leg half-heartedly.

"Look, Mrs. Allen," she said when the pasty, somewhat overweight woman she knew only by sight opened the door, "I don't want to make any trouble, but I'm afraid those boys of yours have been causing damage in my garden."

"My boys?" She grabbed the elastic of her underwear and yanked it up under her stained yellow dress.

"Yes," Dorothy went on. "Someone keeps pushing over my garden ornament, and I'm sure they know something about it."

"My boys, eh? Well, let me tell you something, you snoopy old bat. My Tom's gone out to Calgary to visit his uncle, and Fred's working up north with the forestry. So don't be so bloody quick to blame people what ain't done nothin'." And she slammed the door.

Dorothy stood for a moment at a loss. Her face was hot with embarrassment as she turned and walked down the path, not daring to turn around in case Mrs. Allen was watching her from the window.

Next morning the gnome was gone. At first Dorothy thought he must be concealed among the clump of day lilies at the foot of the rockery, but when she went out to the garden there was no sign of him. This time her anger was mixed with other feelings. She was a little bit afraid, she realized. She looked up and down the empty street, but no curtain moved. Most of the people were at work. She went inside, found the number she kept handy by the phone, and called the police.

"We'll get someone around as soon as we can," said the police operator when she explained there'd been a robbery. He didn't seem to be giving it very high priority. She made herself a cup of coffee and noticed that her hand was shaking as she poured it. She drew the living-room curtains half-way to. When a car pulled up outside she was relieved to see it was Norah, and then she remembered that her friend was leaving that afternoon to visit her sister in Charlottetown and had said she would drop by to say goodbye.

"What a dirty trick!" Norah said when Dorothy told her what had happened, and they went to look at the empty spot where the gnome had stood. A few moments later a young policeman arrived, but he seemed to lose interest when Dorothy explained that it was a garden ornament that had been stolen. "Okay, ma'am," he said, taking out his notebook with a resigned air. "Let's get the particulars."

As he was going out of the door afterwards, he stopped. "Frankly, ma'am, I wouldn't get my hopes up about seeing your gnome again. There's been a lot of vandalism going on, and it's probably kids who've chucked it somewhere now."

"Norah," said Dorothy after closing the door, "would you help me? That's exactly what I was thinking before you arrived. That maybe some kids threw the gnome down the ravine. I know I won't be able to sleep tonight for wondering. But down there's not a place I'd dare to go on my own."

"Well . . . " said her friend looking at her watch. "If we're not too long, because I have to do some things before I catch my plane."

The two women went cautiously down the steep stairs that an over-optimistic parks department had sign-posted "Nature Trail". "Booze Trail" is more like it, Dorothy thought to herself as they picked their way past the beer bottles discarded by teenagers and the empty wine bottles left by the decrepit men in bulging raincoats whom she had seen emerging from the ravine.

"It's just that I'd feel better knowing," said Dorothy as they reached the viaduct. "Even if he's smashed into fragments by now."

Pigeons rattled up noisily at their approach, and as they probed the undergrowth, a man lying on a pile of newspapers startled them by suddenly snorting in his sleep.

"Just don't let this affair get to you," Norah said after they had climbed panting back up the steps. "Look, I'll tell you what we'll do. Next time you come to the cottage, after I get back, we'll go into the garden centre and see if they've got another one."

Back home, Dorothy put on a cheerful front as Norah started her car. "Have a safe trip, dear," she said. "Don't make too much of a pig of yourself at those lobster suppers!"

Walking up the path she couldn't help looking sadly at the vacant spot in the rockery. It became a routine every morning for her. First thing she'd pull back the living-room curtains, half-expecting to see him back there. Darn it, she missed him, just as if he'd been a person. She'd shrug it off and after breakfast get out her gardening gloves and tools and busy herself with the weeding.

The first postcard arrived the following Wednesday. Finding it in the box, she assumed it was from Norah. But instead of a picture of Prince Edward Island, it had a photograph of the Rockies. It was postmarked Calgary, and the message, in a neat, round, almost childish hand, said, "Dear Dorothy, Having a great time. Saw a rodeo yesterday. Wild! Love, Mr. Gnome."

She sat down on the chair in the hallway. Her heart was racing. A trick. It had to be a trick. But who would go to such lengths to scare her?

Two days later there was another postcard in the box, this time from Vancouver. She didn't even bother looking at the picture. "Dearest Dorothy," said the message. "What a wonderful city! You really should see it. Just spectacular! See you soon, Mr. Gnome." The handwriting was the same. Angrily she tore it into pieces until her fingers hurt trying to reduce it to smaller and smaller scraps. She took them into the living room, put them in the fireplace and, lighting a match, watched the blue flame dance until the little heap was reduced to ashes.

She didn't tell Norman about it, but each morning she watched for him to come, sometimes giving him a cheerful greeting, then anxiously going through her mail. To her relief no more cards arrived, except one from Norah. A week went by and she was beginning to forget the whole thing, when one morning a card with a foreign stamp turned up in the mailbox. Without even reading the caption she recognized the picture as that of the flying full wings of the Sydney Opera House.

"Dear Dorothy," she read. "Here I am in Sydney. Never thought I'd make it this far. Australians super-friendly. Love, Mr. Gnome." She walked unsteadily into the dining room, got out the bottle of brandy, and poured herself some in a wine glass. Australian brandy, she noticed with a tiny shudder. Now she knew for certain there would be more cards.

The next one arrived a couple of days later. "Norman!" she called as he walked across the lawn towards next door. "Would you mind coming here a minute?"

"What's the matter, Mrs. Graham?" he said, flicking back his hair. "You look pretty shaken. Bad news?"

"Well, it's not that. But would you mind reading this card for me?"

He gave her a funny look. "Sure, Mrs. Graham. If you want me to." Maybe her eyes were playing up.

"Dear, dear Dorothy," he read in a monotone. "Please don't worry, but I'm laid up with some sort of bug. I'll keep you posted. Love, Mr. Gnome." Norman shook his head. "That's what it says, Mrs. Graham. Funny sort of message. Why is it signed like that?"

She asked him if he wouldn't mind coming inside and, sitting at the kitchen table, she showed him the first card she'd received.

"Look, Mrs. Graham, I don't know who would do a rotten thing like that, but what you've got to do is pay no mind to it. You hear me? It's just someone trying to scare you, eh? Well, don't think about it." He slung his bag over his shoulder as he got up to go. "This is what I'll do. I'll keep an eye open and if any more cards come like that, I'll knock and give it to you so you don't get a scare, like. I mean finding it in the box."

That night Dorothy had a strange, mixed-up dream in which she looked outside and the gnome had come back. Only when she looked again it wasn't the gnome at all, but Ted who was sitting in the middle of the rockery in his pyjamas. "Come on inside, Ted. You'll catch your death," she called. "I can't, Dorothy," he replied. "I'm too ill. Help me, please!" Then he got smaller and smaller, and his voice became squeaky until she could no longer hear or see him.

In the morning Norman met her at the door looking worried. "Fact is, Mrs. Graham, there's another card," she said, handing it to her. It was another view of Sydney. She turned it over quickly. "Dorothy," it said, the handwriting spidery and sprawling now. "So ill. Miss you." The signature was almost illegible, but she knew well enough what it said.

"This really is beyond a joke," she said, leaning her head against the doorpost. "Norman, I think I'm going to call the police about it."

It was an older officer who came this time. She told him her story and showed him the postcards, except for the one she'd burned. "I can see how you'd be upset, ma'am," he said in a kindly voice. "It's a very unpleasant thing to have happen. Is there anyone you can think of who has a grudge against you?"

She couldn't, and finally he left with the same sort of reassurances Norman had given her. "If anything unusual happens, if you see any strangers hanging about the street, anything like that, you just be sure and call us," he said.

Norman looked almost shamefaced when he brought her the postcard next day. "I've read it. I suppose I shouldn't have. But you mustn't get upset," he said handing it to her. "Would you like me to stay while you read it?"

She shook her head. "I'll be okay. Thanks, Norman," she said, and took the card with her other mail into the kitchen. She sat down dully at the table and studied the picture of Sydney harbour for several moments before turning the card over. "Dorothy. Doc says operation my only hope. Pray for me. Feel so bad." The writing trailed off and this time there was no signature. She felt her eyes stinging. She took off her glasses, and put her head down on her arms. "Oh, please," she sobbed. "Leave me alone. Whoever you are."

She worked in the garden most of the day to distract herself, then went out to dinner at the little French restaurant that had just opened at the shopping mall. Coming home, she turned on the television and then, unusual for her, watched not only the eleven o'clock news, but a late movie that didn't end until one. Even then she couldn't sleep when she finally went to bed, so she turned on the light and read a biography of Catherine the Great. It wasn't until three in the morning that her eyes drooped and she reached out sleepily to turn off the bedside light. It seemed as if she hadn't been asleep more than a few minutes when the phone rang. The red glow of the clock radio told her it was 5:14 a.m. Dorothy grabbed her robe from the foot of the bed and, bumping her shoulder on the door, stumbled down the hallway to the phone table.

"Yes, hello," she said.

"Is that Mrs. Dorothy Graham?" It was a male voice, official-sounding and faintly bored.

"Yes, who's calling?"

"This is CNCP Telecommunications. We have a telegram for you. Shall I read it to you?"

"Yes, yes. But just a minute please while I turn the light on. I'll get a pen."

It was unlike Dorothy not to be home at breakfast. Norah let the phone ring a few more times then put down the receiver. She had thought of calling the night before but it had been rather late when she had arrived home from the airport, so she'd waited until the morning. Perhaps Dorothy had taken ill. Norah got her handbag from the bedroom, picked up the car keys from the mantelpiece, and went out to the garage.

She passed the ambulance as it pulled out of Dorothy's street. It didn't seem to be rushing, and there was no siren. Probably dropping someone off, coming home from hospital, Norah thought.

As she walked up the path she was surprised to see a young man in a mailman's uniform sitting on the steps with his head in his hands. "Where's Mrs. Graham?" she asked.

He looked up startled. "They just took her away. Are you Mrs. Graham's friend, the one that was in P.E.I.?"

Norah nodded. "She told me about you," he said. "I'm Norman."

"Well, where on earth did they take her?" she said sharply. "What's the matter?"

"It's terrible really," he said, almost as if he hadn't heard her. "I found her, see. I had another one of those cards for her and I knocked on the door but she didn't come. Well, like, I looked in the window and I could see her lying there on the living-room floor. Right in front of the big window. She wasn't moving, eh? So, well, I went round the back and smashed open the window.

"She just looked sort of blue. I gave her mouth-to-mouth," he went on quickly. "I tried everything, but it wasn't no good. So I called the ambulance. She was gone."

Norah steadied herself against the wall. "Gone?"

"You look pretty shook up. You better come inside and sit down," said Norman. "I'm not feeling too good myself."

They went around to the back, and Norman showed her where he'd broken the window and put in his hand to open the back door. Norah walked through the empty rooms, then back to the kitchen where Norman was making them instant coffee.

"I figure the postcards must have had something to do with it," he said. "That was a dirty trick."

"What postcards?"

"Didn't she write to you about them?" He looked around the kitchen then reached up on the shelf above the sink. "Here they are. Someone took her gnome then started sending her postcards from all over. They're signed 'Mr. Gnome'. Pretty weird, eh?"

Norah read the cards then laid them out on the table in front of her. "This one came only today," said Norman, pulling another card from his pocket and handing it to her. The picture was of

Adelaide. "Dear Dorothy. Just here for a couple of days before returning Sydney. Beautiful spot. Love, Mr. Gnome," the message read.

Norah compared the datemarks. "It must have been held up. It was written before some of the later ones," she said. Norman had put his cup in the sink. "Anyway, I better get back to work. I'm way behind."

"Look Norman," said Norah, making up her mind. "This is all pretty fishy. I think we should call the police. How do we know something didn't happen here last night? You carry on with your route, but I'll stay here for the police. Where can they reach you if they need to?"

"I'll give you my number at home as well as my work number," he said, pulling a red pen out of the holder in his shirt pocket. He looked around for a piece of paper, then pulled over one of the postcards and wrote in an empty space. "See, that's my name, Norman Stannard," he said, handing her the card. "Bye now."

Norah went into the hall to phone, the card still in her hand. As she dialled her eye caught a message scribbled on the pad by the phone. "The gnome died today," it said.

She put the receiver back. Her heart was pounding. She looked at the card in her hand. "Beautiful spot," she read. Something tickled at the back of her brain. Two things trying to come together. She looked at the card again, at the round, childish handwriting. Then she noticed. The writing in which the name and phone numbers had been written above the address.

She got up and went to the front window. Norman, his bag slung over his shoulder, was walking down the street. She could hear him whistling. The tiny hairs on the back of her hands tingled. She knew someone was watching her. She didn't know how it was that she hadn't noticed before: the gnome was back in his old place. His smile had the same insolence she had noticed when she had first seen him at the nursery.

Responding

1. Through whose eyes is most of the story told? Where does the point of view change? What is the purpose of having two parts?

2. Before the content of the telegram is revealed at the end of the story, clues are given as to what it might read. What are these clues?

3. What acts of kindness are attributed to Norman? Why does the author emphasize Norman's good qualities?

4. Was Norman intending Mr. Gnome's messages to be an innocent joke? Comment. How does he seem to react to Dorothy's death?

5. What qualities make this story entertaining?

6. Would this story make a good movie? Why or why not?

7. The story illustrates that people are sometimes different from what we believe them to be. Tell about a time when your view of someone changed.

Student notes, page 241

Yves Thériault

THE WHALE

A simple, honest fisherman struggles against the skepticism of an entire village—and makes the biggest catch of his life.

O n every boot and quay from Gaspé to Paspébiac the news spread like wildfire: Ambroise Bourdages claimed that— singlehandedly—he had landed a whale!

The fishermen were all getting a great kick out of it. Now if Ambroise had claimed that he had caught a two-hundred pound cod that had later managed to get free of the hook, everyone would have made a solemn show of believing it. That would have been an admissible exaggeration, quite in keeping with local instincts, habits, and customs . . . But a whale?

Stretching his arms wide Ambroise insisted: "I'm telling you, a whale! Colossal! As big as a boat—bigger even! Ahhh, my friends, my friends . . . I spot it sunning itself. Quick as I can I grab a rope, I get a hook on it, I bait it with a herring, I attach a floater, and then I let it out behind the boat . . . the whale spies the bait and starts

24

making for it. I let out the line . . . a hundred, two hundred feet.
The whale swallows the bait—and it's hooked!"

"This hook of yours, how big is it?" asked Vilmont Babin.

"A big cod hook. Maybe an inch and a half . . ."

"And it hooked the whale?"

"Yes."

A tremendous burst of laughter shook the whole quay.

About a dozen fishermen were listening as Ambroise related his
adventure. A few girls were there too, as there always are when the
boats come in. Among them was Gabrielle, who smiled too much at
Adélard these days—at least in the opinion of Ambroise, who had
eyes only for her.

Unlike the others, who found his story too good—and too funny
—to be true, she listened gravely and did not laugh.

There was a look in Gabrielle's eyes that Ambroise could not
quite make out. It was a serious expression that suited her natural
reserve and good manners—manners very different from those of
the rude, obnoxious Adélard.

He was there too, laughing with the others at Ambroise, making
fun of him.

"Did you stow your whale in the hold?" he asked Ambroise. "Or
weren't you strong enough to haul such a big trophy into your
boat?"

This produced a great roar of laughter. Everyone wanted to slap
Adélard on the back. Here was a match for Ambroise! Someone
with the answer to a tall tale!

"Call me a liar," he said with dignity, "it doesn't bother me. Just
remember this: if I were on my deathbed and my mother asked me
to repeat every word I've just told you, I'd do it. I didn't lie to you.
My men were asleep below. We were heading out towards the
Shippegan banks and I was at the tiller. I landed a whale . . . and
anyone who doesn't believe me can forget it. I know what I did. I
hooked a whale with a cod-hook."

He spat on the timbers of the quay, turned on his heel, and left.

Naturally it wasn't long before they were talking about Ambroise
Bourdages's alleged miraculous catch in every village on the Coast.
As it made the rounds from one quay to another the story was
altered and embellished out of all recognition. Ambroise was
floored by the version that got back to him.

25

It was Clovis, the prissy, affected son of the banker in Port-Savoie, where Ambroise lived, who brought back the first of this bizarre gossip.

"Do you know what they're saying at Paspébiac?" he asked Ambroise. "My poor friend, you'd never believe it! It's really terrible!"

"What are they saying?"

"I said it's terrible, but to tell the truth it's mostly funny."

"Let's say it *is* funny. What is it?"

"Good heavens you're tiresome! So impatient ... Well, to hear them talk it seems you caught a whale with your bare hands, held on to it for dear life all by yourself, fought like the devil to haul it by the tail into your boat, and in the end it got away."

Ambroise groaned.

"Ah, no, no! They're all making fun of me!"

Just at that moment Gabrielle came out of the Company store. Her hair floated on the breeze and her smile was as bright as a sunflower.

"How beautiful she is," thought Ambroise, "so tall and graceful. If only she could like me!"

But as she passed close by Ambroise she gave a sarcastic little laugh.

"I have to get proof of my story!" cried Ambroise, when Gabrielle was out of earshot. "Clovis, no one would ever take you for a liar! A banker's son isn't allowed to tell lies!"

"Of course I mustn't tell lies. Lying isn't nice. Besides, I wouldn't want to disgrace my father."

"All right then! Tomorrow you and I are going out to sea. You'll be my witness. We're going to catch another whale, and this time it won't get away!"

Next day they headed out on the water. Despite the sunshine the seas were heavy and sullen. The boat rolled and pitched for seven long miles. But then, just at the end of the run, they saw a jet of spray rising from a whale that was frolicking in the waves—not six yards from the boat.

To summarize the day's adventures we'll say that Ambroise, using all his fisherman's skill, managed to catch the whale with his cod-hook. This was not easily done. The sea monster gave a magnificent display of its strength and agility. On three different occasions, while diving furiously in an effort to get free of the hook, the whale almost capsized the boat. Finally exhausted, it rose calmly to the surface. Ambroise fastened the rope and took the tiller. Slowly he towed his trophy towards the moorings of Port-Savoie.

He was bursting with joy. It had been accomplished despite all the doubt and sarcasm. Even Gabrielle would have to agree that he, Ambroise Bourdages, had not lied about capturing a whale. In fact it was so far from being a lie that a week later he had gone out and caught another.

This was the way to silence the scandalmongers.

At the same time it ought to establish him as the greatest fisherman and the most respected man on the Coast.

It is not every day that a man catches a whale with such simple tackle. And even if there is an element of luck in it, there is also an element of know-how and gumption that cannot be overlooked.

But just as they were about a mile from Port-Savoie the whale suddenly came to life. With one powerful sneeze it spat out the hook—as if to show that it had only been toying with them and could quite easily have escaped earlier, if it had wanted to.

Then it dived and disappeared under the water.

This loss, however, did not bother Ambroise too much.

He had a witness with him. An honest man, a banker's son, a person to corroborate his story who would be believed without question.

As he jumped up onto the quay he let out a great cry.

"Ahoy!"

About fifty people, all aware of the expedition, were waiting when Ambroise and Clovis returned.

Even Gabrielle was there.

Ambroise quickly told what had happened. He described everything in detail. And as the ripples of laughter began to spread: "Listen Ambroise," said Vilmont Babin, "you can get away with it once, but the same lie twice—it won't work!"

With a great sweep of his arm Ambroise pointed to Clovis.

"Clovis was there. He's my witness. An honest witness. He saw it all. He'll tell you that the whale got away just about a mile from here."

But Clovis was sporting a smile that looked more like a grin.

Then, in his piping voice he declared: "Ambroise is a liar. I never saw him catch a whale!"

The shouts and threats that followed this declaration were so clamorous, and poor Ambroise was so crushed by Clovis's double-dealing, that all he could think of was to run away as fast as possible.

Two hours later he risked going outside again. Clovis was standing by the Post Office. Ambroise hurried over to him. The young man waited for him imperturbably.

"Snake in the grass!" Ambroise yelled at him. "Liar! Worse—you're a perjurer! I'll have you arrested!"

"Just a minute, my friend," said Clovis stiffly. "There's something you don't know. I have my eye on Gabrielle too. Do you really think I'm going to let you impress her with your whale-fishing story? I've decided to fight—with my own weapons! The fortunes of war, old fellow, I'm sorry."

But Ambroise, disconsolate, had already left. He felt trapped, beaten. Farewell dreams! He'd lost Gabrielle forever to wilier men. Clovis, for one. And Adélard. While he, Ambroise, was fighting shadows.

Once again he raced for home.

But as he was entering the house the sun suddenly reappeared and joy began to revive his hopes. Gabrielle was there, in the kitchen, with Ambroise's mother.

"Ah!" said Ambroise ... "Gabrielle?"

She smiled at him.

"Ambroise, I apologize. Forgive me ... I misunderstood your lie about the whale!"

"But," said Ambroise, "it wasn't a ...."

Gabrielle waved aside his explanation.

"When you tried to tell your story for the second time today, I admit I was disgusted. I knew you were trying to impress me. But after I got home I began to think about it. Do you know what I decided, Ambroise?"

"No ... no."

"It's a lucky girl that has a fellow who'll go against everyone just for her, simply to impress her, to win her ...."

Ambroise was about to protest strongly again, but suddenly he thought better of it. A sly gleam appeared in his eye. So this was the way the land lay? Well, then.

"Gabrielle," he said softly, "it was the least I could do. A lie like that about a cod would never have been enough—not grand enough! But a whale, an impossible catch ... It was a matter of gallantry, of giving it enough weight—you know?"

"Of course. That's why I'm here ..."

So Ambroise took her by the hand and led her out into the village and walked with her so that everyone would plainly see that in spite of everything he'd made the best catch of his life ... and to hell with the whale!

Translated by Patricia Sillers

Responding

1. This story might be described as a series of events that each turn out differently from what we expect. Describe each event and its unexpected outcome.

2. Describe the various emotions Ambroise experiences in the course of the story. What do these emotions reveal about his personality?

3. What keeps the reader interested in reading the story through to the ending?

4. What does "The Whale" reveal about the community in which it is set?

5. The story illustrates one reason people might fall in love. Brainstorm other reasons people may fall in love. Which, in your view, are the most common reasons? Comment.

Student notes, page 241

2 PLOT AND CONFLICT

Most of our actions in life are determined by our needs, wants, and goals. Our concerns might be as basic as satisfying hunger or finding relief from pain; however, they may be as complicated as succeeding in a career or coming to a new understanding of ourselves. Whether basic or complicated, our needs, wants, and goals give us something to work toward, a motivation for our actions.

Story characters are similar to us. They too have needs, wants, and goals. Stories generally focus on a single concern of a character and usually follow the character's thoughts and actions as he or she seeks to fulfill that need, satisfy that want, or achieve that goal. As in life, the characters in stories cannot always get what they want without some struggle, and sometimes they are defeated by impossible obstacles. Those forces that stand in the way create conflict that we and the characters in fiction must resolve in order to move toward the aim we have set for ourselves. Usually, a story is over when an outcome is made clear. As in life, a character may succeed or fail, or there may be no clear outcome because the character's problem is not solvable.

An important benefit of reading stories is learning about the problems other people face, the strategies they use to resolve conflicts, and their feelings about their experiences. When we measure these elements against our own experiences and beliefs, we may learn more about ourselves and others.

The stories in this unit reveal three very different conflicts. The first is a life-and-death struggle, the second portrays a troubled father-son relationship, and the third takes place entirely within the mind of a participant at a family dinner. The differing concerns of the characters in these stories reflect in a small way the unlimited variety of conflicts in literature. We can see as we continue to read other stories and novels that the conflicts in literature mirror the complex and fascinating struggles that are part of life.

Arthur Gordon

THE SEA DEVIL

Nighttime on a Florida bay. A lone man in a rowboat casts his net on still waters, unaware of a deadly danger lurking just below the surface . . .

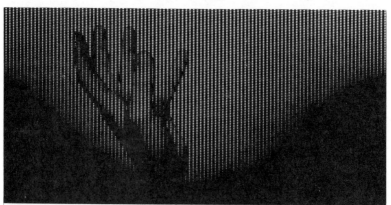

*T*he man came out of the house and stood quite still, listening. Behind him, the lights glowed in the cheerful room, the books were neat and orderly in their cases, the radio talked importantly to itself. In front of him, the bay stretched dark and silent, one of the countless lagoons that border the coast where Florida thrusts its great green thumb deep into the tropics.

It was late in September. The night was breathless; summer's dead hand still lay heavy on the land. The man moved forward six paces and stood on the sea wall. He dropped his cigarette and noted where the tiny spark hissed and went out. The tide was beginning to ebb.

Somewhere out in the blackness a mullet jumped and fell back with a sullen splash. Heavy with roe, they were jumping less often, now. They would not take a hook, but a practised eye could see the swirls they made in the glassy water. In the dark of the moon, a skilled man with a cast net might take half a dozen in an hour's work. And a big mullet makes a meal for a family.

32

The man turned abruptly and went into the garage, where his cast net hung. He was in his late twenties, wide-shouldered and strong. He did not have to fish for a living, or even for food. He was a man who worked with his head, not with his hands. But he liked to go casting alone at night.

He liked the loneliness and the labor of it. He liked the clean taste of salt when he gripped the edge of the net with his teeth as a cast netter must. He liked the arching flight of sixteen pounds of lead and linen against the starlight, and the weltering crash of the net into the unsuspecting water. He liked the harsh tug of the retrieving rope around his wrist, and the way the net came alive when the cast was true, and the thud of captured fish on the floorboards of the skiff.

He liked all that because he found in it a reality that seemed to be missing from his twentieth-century job and from his daily life. He liked being the hunter, skilled and solitary and elemental. There was no conscious cruelty in the way he felt. It was the way things had been in the beginning.

The man lifted the net down carefully and lowered it into a bucket. He put a paddle beside the bucket. Then he went into the house. When he came out, he was wearing swimming trunks and a pair of old tennis shoes. Nothing else.

The skiff, flat-bottomed, was moored off the sea wall. He would not go far, he told himself. Just to the tumbledown dock half a mile away. Mullet had a way of feeding around old pilings after dark. If he moved quietly, he might pick up two or three in one cast close to the dock. And maybe a couple of others on the way down or back.

He shoved off and stood motionless for a moment, letting his eyes grow accustomed to the dark. Somewhere out in the channel a porpoise blew with a sound like steam escaping. The man smiled a little; porpoises were his friends. Once, fishing in the Gulf he had seen the charter-boat captain reach overside and gaff a baby porpoise through the sinewy part of the tail. He had hoisted it aboard, had dropped it into the bait well, where it thrashed around, puzzled and unhappy. And the mother had swum alongside the boat and under the boat and around the boat, nudging the stout planking with her back, slapping it with her tail, until the man felt sorry for her and made the captain let the baby porpoise go.

He took the net from the bucket, slipped the noose in the

retrieving rope over his wrist, pulled the slipknot tight. It was an old net, but still serviceable; he had rewoven the rents made by underwater snags. He coiled the thirty-foot rope carefully, making sure there were no kinks. A tangled rope, he knew, would spoil any cast.

The basic design of the net had not changed in three thousand years. It was a mesh circle with a diameter of fourteen feet. It measured close to fifteen yards around the circumference and could, if thrown perfectly, blanket a hundred and fifty square feet of sea water. In the center of this radial trap was a small iron collar where the retrieving rope met the twenty-three separate drawstrings leading to the outer rim of the net. Along this rim, spaced an inch and a half apart, were the heavy lead sinkers.

The man raised the iron collar until it was a foot above his head. The net hung soft and pliant and deadly. He shook it gently, making sure that the drawstrings were not tangled, that the sinkers were hanging true. Then he eased it down and picked up the paddle.

The night was black as a witch's cat; the stars looked fuzzy and dim. Down to the southward, the lights of a causeway made a yellow necklace across the sky. To the man's left were the tangled roots of a mangrove swamp; to his right, the open waters of the bay. Most of it was fairly shallow, but there were channels eight feet deep. The man could not see the old dock, but he knew where it was. He pulled the paddle quietly through the water, and the phosphorescence glowed and died.

For five minutes he paddled. Then, twenty feet ahead of the skiff, a mullet jumped. A big fish, close to three pounds. For a moment it hung in the still air, gleaming dully. Then it vanished. But the ripples marked the spot, and where there was one there were often others.

The man stood up quickly. He picked up the coiled rope, and with the same hand grasped the net at a point four feet below the iron collar. He raised the skirt to his mouth, gripped it strongly with his teeth. He slid his free hand as far as it would go down the circumference of the net so that he had three points of contact with the mass of cordage and metal. He made sure his feet were planted solidly. Then he waited, feeling the tension that is older than the human race, the fierce exhilaration of the hunter at the moment of ambush, the atavistic desire to capture and kill and ultimately consume.

A mullet swirled, ahead and to the left. The man swung the heavy net back, twisting his body and bending his knees so as to get more upward thrust. He shot it forward, letting go simultaneously with rope hand and with teeth, holding a fraction of a second longer with the other hand so as to give the net the necessary spin, impart the centrifugal force that would make it flare into a circle. The skiff ducked sideways, but he kept his balance. The net fell with a splash.

The man waited for five seconds. Then he began to retrieve it, pulling in a series of sharp jerks so that the drawstrings would gather the net inward, like a giant fist closing on this segment of the teeming sea. He felt the net quiver, and knew it was not empty. He swung it, dripping, over the gunwale, saw the broad silver side of the mullet quivering, saw too the gleam of a smaller fish. He looked closely to make sure no stingray was hidden in the mesh, then raised the iron collar and shook the net out. The mullet fell with a thud and flapped wildly. The other victim was an angelfish, beautifully marked, but too small to keep. The man picked it up gently and dropped it overboard. He coiled the rope, took up the paddle. He would cast no more until he came to the dock.

The skiff moved on. At last, ten feet apart, a pair of stakes rose up gauntly out of the night. Barnacle-encrusted, they once had marked the approach from the main channel. The man guided the skiff between them, then put the paddle down softly. He stood up, reached for the net, tightened the noose around his wrist. From here he could drift down upon the dock. He could see it now, a ruined skeleton in the starshine. Beyond it a mullet jumped and fell back with a flat, liquid sound. The man raised the edge of the net, put it between his teeth. He would not cast a single swirl, he decided; he would wait until he saw two or three close together. The skiff was barely moving. He felt his muscles tense themselves, awaiting the signal from the brain.

Behind him in the channel he heard the porpoise blow again, nearer now. He frowned in the darkness. If the porpoise chose to fish this area, the mullet would scatter and vanish. There was no time to lose.

A school of sardines surfaced suddenly, skittering along like drops of mercury. Something, perhaps the shadow of the skiff, had frightened them. The old dock loomed very close. A mullet broke water just too far away; then another, nearer. The man marked the spreading ripples and decided to wait no longer.

He swung back the net, heavier now that it was wet. He had to turn his head, but out of the corner of his eye he saw two swirls in the black water just off the starboard bow. They were about eight feet apart, and they had the sluggish oily look that marks the presence of something big just below the surface. His conscious mind had no time to function, but instinct told him that the net was wide enough to cover both swirls if he could alter the direction of his cast. He could not halt the swing, but he shifted his feet slightly and made the cast off balance. He saw the net shoot forward, flare into an oval, and drop just where he wanted it.

Then the sea exploded in his face. In a frenzy of spray, a great horned thing shot like a huge bat out of the water. The man saw the mesh of his net etched against the mottled blackness of its body and he knew, in the split second in which thought was still possible, that those twin swirls had been made not by two mullet, but by the wing tips of the giant ray of the Gulf Coast, *Manta birostris*, also known as clam cracker, devil ray, sea devil.

The man gave a hoarse cry. He tried to claw the slipknot off his wrist, but there was no time. The quarter-inch line snapped taut. He shot over the side of the skiff as if he had roped a runaway locomotive. He hit the water head first and seemed to bounce once. He plowed a blinding furrow for perhaps ten yards. Then the line went slack as the sea devil jumped again. It was not the full-grown manta of the deep Gulf, but it was close to nine feet from tip to tip and it weighed over a thousand pounds. Up into the air it went, pearl-colored underbelly gleaming as it twisted in a frantic effort to dislodge the clinging thing that had fallen upon it. Up into the starlight, a monstrous survival from the dawn of time.

The water was less than four feet deep. Sobbing and choking, the man struggled for a foothold on the slimy bottom. Sucking in great gulps of air, he fought to free himself from the rope. But the slipknot was jammed deep into his wrist; he might as well have tried to loosen a circle of steel.

The ray came down with a thunderous splash and drove forward again. The flexible net followed every movement, impeding it hardly at all. The man weighed a hundred and seventy-five pounds, and he was braced for the shock, and he had the desperate strength that comes from looking into the blank eyes of death. It was useless. His arm straightened out with a jerk that seemed to dislocate his shoulder; his feet shot out from under him; his head went under again. Now at last he knew how the fish must feel when the line tightens and drags him toward the alien element that is his doom. Now he knew.

Desperately he dug the fingers of his free hand into the ooze, felt them dredge a futile channel through broken shells and the ribbon-like sea grasses. He tried to raise his head, but could not get it clear. Torrents of spray choked him as the ray plunged toward deep water.

His eyes were of no use to him in the foam-streaked blackness. He closed them tight, and at once an insane sequence of pictures flashed through his mind. He saw his wife sitting in their living room, reading, waiting calmly for his return. He saw the mullet he had just caught, gasping its life away on the floor boards of the skiff. He saw the cigarette he had flung from the sea wall touch the water and expire with a tiny hiss. He saw all these things and many others simultaneously in his mind as his body fought silently and tenaciously for its existence. His hand touched something hard and closed on it in a death grip, but it was only the sharp-edged helmet of a horseshoe crab, and after an instant he let it go.

He had been under the water perhaps fifteen seconds now, and something in his brain told him quite calmly that he could last another forty or fifty and then the red flashes behind his eyes would merge into darkness, and the water would pour into his lungs in one sharp painful shock, and he would be finished.

This thought spurred him to a desperate effort. He reached up and caught his pinioned wrist with his free hand. He doubled up his knees to create more drag. He thrashed his body madly, like a fighting fish, from side to side. This did not disturb the ray, but now one of the great wings tore through the mesh, and the net slipped lower over the fins projecting like horns from below the nightmare head, and the sea devil jumped again.

And once more the man was able to get his feet on the bottom and his head above water, and he saw ahead of him the pair of ancient stakes that marked the approach to the channel. He knew that if he was dragged much beyond those stakes he would be in eight feet of water, and the ray would go down to hug the bottom as rays always do, and then no power on earth could save him. So in the moment of respite that was granted him, he flung himself toward them. For a moment he thought his captor yielded a bit. Then the ray moved off again, but more slowly now, and for a few yards the man was able to keep his feet on the bottom. Twice he hurled himself back against the rope with all his strength, hoping that something would break. But nothing broke. The mesh of the net was ripped and torn, but the draw lines were strong, and the stout perimeter cord threaded through the sinkers was even stronger.

The man could feel nothing now in his trapped hand, it was numb; but the ray could feel the powerful lunges of the unknown thing that was trying to restrain it. It drove its great wings against the unyielding water and forged ahead, dragging the man and pushing a sullen wave in front of it.

The man had swung as far as he could toward the stakes. He plunged toward one and missed it by inches. His feet slipped and he went down on his knees. Then the ray swerved sharply and the second stake came right at him. He reached out with his free hand and caught it.

He caught it just above the surface, six or eight inches below the high-water mark. He felt the razor-sharp barnacles bite into his hand, collapse under the pressure, drive their tiny slime-covered shell splinters deep into his flesh. He felt the pain, and he welcomed it, and he made his fingers into an iron claw that would hold until the tendons were severed or the skin was shredded from the bone. The ray felt the pressure increase with a jerk that stopped it dead in the water. For a moment all was still as the tremendous forces came into equilibrium.

Then the net slipped again, and the perimeter cord came down over the sea devil's eyes, blinding it momentarily. The great ray settled to the bottom and braced its wings against the mud and hurled itself forward and upward.

The stake was only a four-by-four of creosoted pine, and it was old. Ten thousand tides had swirled around it. Worms had bored;

parasites had clung. Under the crust of barnacles it still had some heart left, but not enough. The man's grip was five feet above the floor of the bay; the leverage was too great. The stake snapped off at its base.

The ray lunged forward, dragging the man and the useless timber. The man had his lungs full of air, but when the stake snapped he thought of expelling the air and inhaling the water so as to have it finished quickly. He thought of this, but he did not do it. And then, just at the channel's edge, the ray met the porpoise coming in.

The porpoise had fed well this night and was in no hurry, but it was a methodical creature and it intended to make a sweep around the old dock before the tide dropped too low. It had no quarrel with any ray, but it feared no fish in the sea, and when the great black shadow came rushing blindly and unavoidably, it rolled fast and struck once with its massive horizontal tail.

The blow descended on the ray's flat body with a sound like a pistol shot. It would have broken a buffalo's back, and even the sea devil was half stunned. It veered wildly and turned back toward shallow water. It passed within ten feet of the man, face down in the water. It slowed and almost stopped, wing tips moving faintly, gathering strength for another rush.

The man had heard the tremendous slap of the great mammal's tail and the snorting gasp as it plunged away. He felt the line go slack again, and he raised his dripping face, and he reached for the bottom with his feet. He found it, but now the water was up to his neck. He plucked at the noose once more with his lacerated hand, but there was no strength in his fingers. He felt the tension come back into the line as the ray began to move again, and for half a second he was tempted to throw himself backward and fight as he had been doing, pitting his strength against the vastly superior strength of the brute.

But the acceptance of imminent death had done something to his brain. It had driven out the fear, and with the fear had gone the panic. He could think now, and he knew with absolute certainty that if he was to make any use of this last chance that had been given him, it would have to be based on the one faculty that had carried man to his pre-eminence above all beasts, the faculty of reason. Only by using his brain could he possibly survive, and he called on his brain for a solution, and his brain responded. It offered him one.

He did not know whether his body still had the strength to carry out the brain's commands, but he began to swim forward, toward the ray that was still moving hesitantly away from the channel. He swam forward, feeling the rope go slack as he gained on the creature.

Ahead of him he saw the one remaining stake, and he made himself swim faster until he was parallel with the ray and the rope trailed behind both of them in a deep U. He swam with a surge of desperate energy that came from nowhere so that he was slightly in the lead as they came to the stake. He passed on one side of it; the ray was on the other.

Then the man took one last deep breath, and he went down under the black water until he was sitting on the bottom of the bay. He put one foot over the line so that it passed under his bent knee. He drove both his heels into the mud, and he clutched the slimy grass with his bleeding hand, and he waited for the tension to come again.

The ray passed on the other side of the stake, moving faster now. The rope grew taut again, and it began to drag the man back toward the stake. He held his prisoned wrist close to the bottom, under his knee, and he prayed that the stake would not break. He felt the rope vibrate as the barnacles bit into it. He did not know whether the rope would crush the barnacles or whether the barnacles would cut the rope. All he knew was that in five seconds or less he would be dragged into the stake and cut to ribbons if he tried to hold on; or drowned if he didn't.

He felt himself sliding slowly, and then faster, and suddenly the ray made a great leap forward, and the rope burned around the base of the stake, and the man's foot hit it hard. He kicked himself backward with his remaining strength, and the rope parted and he was free.

He came slowly to the surface.

Thirty feet away the sea devil made one tremendous leap and disappeared into the darkness. The man raised his wrist and looked at the frayed length of rope dangling from it. Twenty inches, perhaps. He lifted his other hand and felt the hot blood start instantly, but he didn't care. He put this hand on the stake above the barnacles and held on to the good, rough, honest wood. He heard a strange noise, and realized that it was himself, sobbing.

High above, there was a droning sound, and looking up he saw the nightly plane from New Orleans inbound for Tampa. Calm and serene, it sailed, symbol of man's proud mastery over nature. Its lights winked red and green for a moment; then it was gone.

Slowly, painfully, the man began to move through the placid water. He came to the skiff at last and climbed into it. The mullet, still alive, slapped convulsively with its tail. The man reached down with his torn hand, picked up the mullet, let it go.

He began to work on the slip-knot doggedly with his teeth. His mind was almost a blank, but not quite. He knew one thing. He knew he would do no more casting alone at night. Not in the dark of the moon. No, not he.

Responding

1. Why does the man fish by night? How does this lead to the conflict with the ray?

2. What dilemma does the man face before the climax? What enables him to get free of the sea devil?

3. What has the man learned at the end of the story? Why does he release the mullet?

4. One of the conflicts in the story is between the civilized and the primitive. What is the purpose of the reference to the plane, the causeway, and the man's wife at home?

5. Identify the following parts of the story's plot: the complicating incident, a single crisis, the climax, and the resolution.

6. Relate a memorable brush with danger or death you once had.

Student notes, page 242

Hugh Garner

THE FATHER

Johnny and his dad have never been that close. But a trip to the Boy Scout banquet could change their relationship—once and for all.

*I*t wasn't the boy who gave him the invitation, but the boy's mother, his wife. Somehow even a little thing like this had become a shameful chore that the boy had avoided. Over the past year or two father and son had drifted apart, so that a strange shame and embarrassment colored every event that brought them into contact.

His wife had waited until the children had gone out after supper, the boy to play baseball and his older sister to run and scream with other teenagers in the schoolyard. Then she had said, "Johnny wonders if you'll go to the Boy Scout meeting with him tomorrow night?"

It was on the tip of his tongue to say, "Scout meeting! What do I look like?" Instead he asked, "Why, what's on there?"

"It's a father-and-son banquet," she said.

"Why didn't Johnny ask me to go?"

"You know he is—I guess he was too shy," she answered.

"Too shy! Too shy to ask his own father to go somewhere?"

"Well, I guess he was afraid you'd say no," she said.

42

"I'll think it over," he said grudgingly, knowing that he owed it to the boy, and also feeling that it might be a way of overcoming the barrier that had sprung up between them.

He didn't look forward to an evening spent in the company of a bunch of professional fathers, who were "real pals" to their sons. He had seen them making a nuisance of themselves, unable or unwilling to let their kids lead their own lives. They went swimming with their children, tried to umpire their ball games, and wrongly explained the displays at the museum and the animals at the zoo. He wouldn't normally mix with such men, but it was probably a big event for the boy, and it only happened once a year.

He poured himself a small drink and sat before the TV set, thinking of the coolness between him and his son and trying vainly to pinpoint its beginning. He knew that most of the time he was too preoccupied with other things to pay much heed to the boy's activities, but he had dismissed his misgivings with the thought, "He's only a twelve-year-old who wants to be left alone."

Over his drink he remembered the times he had been too harsh with the boy, and the times he had been curt and impatient. And with a feeling of angry revulsion he remembered siding with the teacher when he had been called to the school to discuss the boy's bad marks in reading. The principal had intimated that the boy's slowness might be caused by tensions in the home, but this he had vehemently denied. When the teacher had suggested keeping the boy in the same grade for a second year, he had acquiesced willingly, wanting only to get away from the place. The boy had looked up at him, bitten his lower lip, and had left the principal's office. From then on their distance one from the other was greater than ever.

On the evening of the banquet he was a little late getting home, having stopped in for a few drinks with a customer who was buying an industrial site. He ate warmed-over supper by himself, insisting all the while to his wife that there was no use eating when he was going to a banquet.

"You'd better eat," she said. "You've got to be at your best tonight."

"I'll be at my best, don't worry. I have a couple of drinks with a customer, and you're ready to shove me in an institution."

After he had bathed and shaved he put on his best suit. Though he had only contempt for scoutmasters, he was anxious to create a good impression for the sake of the boy. His suits were getting tight, as were the collars of his shirts. It was sitting at a desk all day did it, and not walking anywhere any more. At the end of the war he had been lean and tough, but now he was middle-aged, fat, with his hair thinning fast on top.

He went downstairs and waited in the living room for the boy. The food his wife had pushed on to him had destroyed the glow from the pre-dinner drinks, so he poured himself a tall one for the road. From upstairs came the sound of his wife and son having their usual spat about the boy combing his hair. Though his wife and children quarrelled often, there was no tension between them at all.

The boy came down, wearing a pair of flannels and a blazer.

"Where's your scout uniform, Johnny?" he asked.

"We don't have to wear it if we don't want to," the boy said.

"I'll bet most of the other kids'll be wearing theirs."

The little boy shrugged.

His wife said, "Leave him alone, John. The reason he isn't wearing his uniform is that he only has half of it."

He couldn't remember how the boy had been dressed on Scout Night.

"Why hasn't he got the whole thing?" he asked his wife angrily. "We're not on the welfare, are we? Surely we could spend a few dollars for a complete scout uniform."

"Yes, but after you bought him the hockey pads and the rifle last Christmas he was afraid to ask you for anything else. He has the pants, belt and shirt, and all he needs is the neckerchief—"

"Afraid to ask me! That's all I hear around this place. What's the matter with this family anyway? God knows what the neighbors must think of me."

"There's no use getting angry," his wife said. "He'll have the whole uniform before long. He doesn't really need it tonight."

"Jimmy Agnew and Don Robertson aren't going to wear their uniform," the boy said, trying to mollify him.

He wondered angrily if the scoutmaster thought he was too cheap to buy the boy a uniform. Probably he said to his assistants, "It's too bad about little Johnny Purcell, isn't it? There's a kid been

coming here for four months now and he still hasn't got a uniform."
He felt a twinge of indigestion as he pictured the scoutmasters—a couple of big sissies running around in short pants playing woodsmen.

He said to his wife, "Listen, Helen, for God's sake take him downtown with you tomorrow and get the rest of the Boy Scout outfit. I don't want those goons down at the church thinking I'm too cheap to buy him one."

He expected the boy's face to light up at this, but he stood in the doorway wearing a blank expression. It was the same look the boy put on when he and his wife quarrelled, or when he had too much to drink and tried to talk to the kid man to man.

When they left the house, his daughter shouted after them, "Thank goodness we're getting rid of the men for the rest of the evening," and she and her mother laughed. The remark irritated him by pointing up the infrequency of such occasions.

As they walked down the street, he felt a warm pride as he stole glances down at the boy. Everyone said the youngster was the spit and image of himself when he was younger, and they both bore the same first name. Fatherhood was the rounding out of a life, probably what was meant in the Bible by a person having to be born again. But even as he thought these things, he knew it was only a fuzzy sentimentality brought on by what he had drunk.

The boy strode along beside him, his hands shoved deep into his pockets, even now managing to convey the distance that separated them. He wanted to get the boy into conversation, but could think of nothing to talk about that wouldn't sound wooden and contrived. He knew there must be a common plane of interest somewhere if he only knew what it was. The boy seemed content to walk along in silence, so he retreated into his own thoughts as they entered the business street that led to the church.

As they passed the schoolyard he asked the boy how the softball team was doing.

"All right. We beat the Tigers yesterday."

"What score?"

"Fifteen-eight."

"Say, that's great! Did you score any runs?"

"One, on Jimmy Agnew's two-bagger."

"Great! Did you put many guys out?"

"No."

He realized that he didn't even know what position his own son played, or even the name of the team. He thought it might be the Cardinals, but it might even be the Eskimos. He tried to picture the name on the front of the boy's sweater, but could not recall it.

"How many more games do you play?" he asked.

"Just two more in the regular schedule, one with the Eskimos tomorrow night, and one on Saturday with the Cardinals."

Well, the team wasn't the Tigers, Eskimos or Cardinals. He tried without success to think of the names of the other teams in the league. When they got home he'd have to take a peek at the name on the sweater.

They walked the rest of the way to the church in silence.

A young man in a clerical collar greeted them at the door to the parish hall, introducing himself as Mr. Redpath, the curate.

"My name's John Purcell," he said, smiling and shaking the curate's hand.

"How do you do. Though I know Johnny, and also Mrs. Purcell and your daughter Joanne, this is the first time I've had the pleasure of meeting you, I believe."

"Yes it is."

He was a little put out to discover that his family had a life separate from his. Of course they went to church fairly regularly, while he never went at all. When he was asked if he attended church he always answered, "Not since I was marched there with the army."

The young curate didn't seem to know what to do now that they had been introduced. He turned to the boy and asked, "How is the swimming coming along, Johnny?"

"Fine, Mr. Redpath."

The curate said, "He's going to be a great swimmer someday, is your son."

"Yes I know," he answered. Though he was aware that the boy had been going two nights a week to a neighborhood high school pool, he had never thought of him being an exceptional swimmer. He seemed to know less about the boy than anyone.

They were interrupted by the appearance of the scoutmaster, a very tall man with glasses, wearing a Boy Scout shirt and long khaki trousers.

Mr. Redpath said, "Mr. Purcell, I'd like you to meet Bob Wooley, the scoutmaster."

"How do you do," he said, putting out his hand. He noticed the two Second World War medal ribbons on the man's left breast, and knew the scoutmaster had never left the country.

The man peered at him as he took his hand. "I'm sorry, I didn't catch the name," he said.

"Purcell," he told him, his smile frozen on his lips.

"Oh yes, Johnny Purcell's father!"

He managed an amiable nod, but decided that the scoutmaster had come up to expectations.

"Well, Mr. Purcell, I have a disagreeable duty to perform," the man said, pulling a sheaf of tickets from the pocket of his shirt. Holding out two of them he said, "That will be three dollars please," giggling at the curate.

He decided to get into the spirit of the thing, and as he reached for his wallet he said, "Three dollars! Why I could have taken Johnny to a burlesque show for less than that."

The curate and the scoutmaster snickered politely, but he noticed them exchange significant glances. He handed over the money and pocketed the tickets.

"Right upstairs, Mr. Purcell," Redpath said, his tone much cooler than it had been.

When he looked around for the boy, he found he had disappeared, and he climbed to the banquet hall alone.

It was a large room, probably used for the Sunday-school. It had an odor of sanctity about it, an almost forgotten smell of hymnbooks and varnish that carried him back to his choir-boy days. Down the middle of the floor stretched two long plank tables supported on sawhorses, and covered with paper tablecloths. There were about fifty places set. Hanging on the walls were various exhibits of scoutcraft, and in one corner of the floor a tent and an imitation campfire had been set up, surrounded by imitation grass probably borrowed from the church cemetery next door.

He spied his son, in the company of two other boys and their fathers, looking at some photographs on the wall, and walked over to them. As soon as he reached his side, Johnny led him away from the others and began pointing out the various knots that were illustrated by twisted pieces of sashcord mounted on a board.

"Have you anything on exhibition, Johnny?" he asked the boy.

"Only the Cree mask I made last winter."

Cree mask! He'd never seen the boy making a mask, though he had wondered vaguely what he was doing in the basement sometimes. "Let's go over and see it," he said, and the boy led him around the tables to the opposite wall.

They stopped before a wooden mask, painted red and yellow with holes cut in it for the eyes and mouth. He was no judge of such things, but he was amazed at the workmanship and artistry of it. He could see the tremendous amount of work that had gone into its carving, and felt an immeasurable loss as he realized he had not even inquired what the boy was doing all those long evenings in the basement.

"Say, Johnny, that's great! It's just great!" he said, slapping his son on the shoulder. "I never knew you could make things like that. Did you carve it out of a single piece of wood?"

"No. I had to glue two pieces together."

"Where did you get it—the wood I mean?"

"Mr. Robertson gave me it. He helped me shape it, but I did most of the carving."

"Who's Mr. Robertson?"

"Don's dad. *You* know Don Robertson." "Oh sure." He didn't know one boy or girl who came to the house from another. It must be the tall blond kid who went to the movies with Johnny on Saturday afternoons.

Two boys and their fathers came along and stood beside them, admiring the mask. He was about to tell them it was the work of his boy, but Johnny was suddenly in a hurry to get away. "Come on, Dad," he said quickly. "There's a picture over here of Danny Mahaffey winning his mountaineer badge."

He followed the boy to the end of the room, aware for the first time that his son was ashamed of him. As he pretended to look at the photograph, he wondered what he had ever done to make the boy feel that way. Now he remembered the times he had met Johnny with his friends on the street, and had received only a grudging wave of the hand from him. And he remembered going to watch the boy play ball in the schoolyard, and being pointedly ignored throughout the game.

The dinner consisted of the usual creamed chicken and peas, and the after-dinner speeches contained the usual intramural jokes shared by the scoutmaster, the curate and the boys. During the meal he became quite friendly with the father sitting on his right, not realizing until it was too late that he had acted over-loquacious, his earlier drinks, plus the heat of the hall, making him talk and laugh too loudly. Once he stopped himself in time before criticizing the scoutmaster's home-service ribbons.

Johnny hardly spoke to him at all, but attached himself conversationally to a boy sitting on the other side of him. They laughed at the speakers' jokes and whispered conspiratorially, ignoring him completely.

From the anecdotes of the speakers, he was surprised to find that many of the fathers had visited the summer camp, and that some even joined in the weekend hikes. He had been under the impression that only the scoutmaster and his assistant went along with the boys. He began to feel like an outsider, and he glanced along the line of adult faces across the table, wondering if he was alone in his feelings. Every other father had the look of belonging.

Just when the curate's stories were beginning to gripe him, that young man ended his speech and announced a five-minute break before the presentations would be made. With a loud clattering of chairs, the boys and their fathers pushed themselves away from the tables.

When he looked around for Johnny he saw him running towards the stairway in company with the boy who had been sitting beside him. He pushed his way through the crowd to the back door of the hall, and stood on the outside steps and lit a cigarette.

The door behind him opened and a man came out.

"It's kind of stuffy in there," the man said.

"Yes, in more ways than one."

The man laughed. "You said it. This is the first time I ever came to one of these things."

"Me too."

"Good. I was afraid I was the only one."

"My name's Purcell—John Purcell," he said, offering the other his hand.

"Glad to know you, John. I'm Charley Murdoch—Murdoch's

49

Radio and Appliances up on Lorimer Street."

"Sure, I've seen your place."

"What line of business are you in?"

"I'm with Saunders, Gordon and Company, real estate and industrial appraisers."

"Fine."

Murdoch lit a cigarette and they stood talking about the Boy Scouts and their unfamiliarity with dinners such as this one. They discovered they had a couple of mutual friends downtown.

Then Murdoch said, "This may not be the exact place for it, but I've got a bottle of liquor in the car. Would you care for a snort before we go back to hear how the curate got marooned on the island in Elk Lake, or how the scoutmaster's tent blew down in the storm last summer?"

"You're a lifesaver," he said.

They walked to Murdoch's car, which was parked against the cemetery wall. Murdoch took a pint of whiskey from the glove compartment, and then began to feel around in the back seat. "I've got a small bottle of gingerale back here somewhere," he said. "Yeah, here she is!" He straightened up and took the top off the ginger-ale with a practised motion beneath the dashboard.

They had three good drinks apiece before Murdoch said, "Maybe we'd better go back inside. If we don't get in there soon that kid of mine will tell his mother for sure."

The presentations were well under way by the time they returned to the hall, and there was a craning of necks by almost everyone as they crossed the floor. As each boy's name was called, he and his father would go forward to the dais, where the scoutmaster presented the badges to the father, who then presented them to his son.

Johnny gave him an apprehensive look when he sat down, and then crowded as far away from him as he could get, trying to associate himself with the boy and his father on the other side of him.

He sat back in his chair and gave his attention to what was taking place on the platform, smiling to himself as the boys and their fathers left the tables, received their presentations, and returned to their seats. As the whiskey began to work, he took a friendlier view of the affair, and applauded heartily as each twosome sat down. He mentioned to his neighbor that it looked like an investiture at Buckingham Palace, but the man shushed him with a finger placed to his lips. Once, he tried to catch Murdoch's eye, but his new friend was looking somewhere else.

When the assistant scoutmaster called out, "John Purcell," he tapped his son on the shoulder and stood up, saying, "That's both of us." There were a few titters from the boys, and a couple of the fathers smiled. Johnny hurried to the platform without waiting for him. He followed, grinning at the upturned faces he passed. Now that he was on his feet the room began to blur, and the faces at the tables seemed to run together into one big bemused grin. He grinned back, feeling a fellowship with every other father in the room. They really weren't a bad bunch once you got to know them.

As he climbed the steps to the dais the scoutmasters stared at him with a quizzical look, and the curate turned to the audience with an embarrassed smile. The scoutmaster approached him and said, "Mr. Purcell, I am happy and honored to present this lifesaving certificate to your son, John Purcell, and also this badge for hobby-craft. It is not very often that a boy as young as John earns a lifesaving certificate, and I'm sure you must be very proud of him."

He nodded his head and murmured his thanks. When he looked down to face the boy, the room swam before his eyes, but he managed to stay erect. "Here you are, Johnny," he said, handing the boy the certificate and badge. He felt prouder than he had ever felt in his life before, and just handing the awards to his son like this didn't seem enough to mark the moment. In a paroxysm of pride and happiness he grasped the boy's hand, and facing the audience, held it aloft like a referee signifying the winner of a boxing bout.

There was a short burst of embarrassed laughter from the tables. He turned to the scoutmaster, who was trying to smile with little success. The boy broke away from him and ran back to his chair, his chin lowered on his chest.

He stepped down carefully from the dais, and, with all the dignity at his command, made his way to his table. As he turned around its end, he staggered slightly and fell against it, pushing the planks askew from the saw-horse that supported them. Two or three of the fathers prevented the whole thing from toppling, but a vase of flowers and a couple of plates fell to the floor with a loud crash.

After apologizing profusely to those who were picking up the flowers from the floor, he reached his chair with extra-careful steps and sat down. Some of the small boys stared at him wonderingly, but their fathers showed an absorbing interest in what was going on upon the platform. He now saw the humor of the accident, and turned to wink at his son to show that everything had turned out all right after all. The boy was sobbing silently, his thin shoulders shuddering beneath his blazer.

Suddenly he was shamed by the enormity of his act, and had to prevent himself from taking his son on his knee and comforting him as he had done when the boy was younger. He pulled himself together instead, setting his mouth in a defiant line, and stared unseeing at the people on the platform.

When the meeting came to an end, he was the first person out of the hall. He walked about fifty yards down the street and stood in the shadows of the cemetery wall. The boy hurried down the steps and came running towards him, and, when he drew abreast, he stepped out and took him by the arm.

"I'm sorry, Johnny," he said, placing his arm around the small boy's shoulders. "I acted a little silly in there, but it was really nothing. It'll be forgotten in a day or two."

The boy turned his tear-stained face up to him and said, "Leave me alone, Daddy, please."

"Look, Johnny, I'm sorry. I didn't mean to hurt you like that. Listen, I'll tell you what we'll do—we'll go downtown tomorrow and I'll buy you a whole new Boy Scout outfit."

"I'm not going to the Scouts any more."

"Sure you are. Listen, you've got that lifesaving certificate and—"

"I left them behind. I don't want them any more."

"But, Johnny, listen—"

"Leave me alone, Daddy, please!" the boy cried, breaking away from him and running down the street.

"Johnny! Wait for me. Johnny! Listen, I want—"

The boy was half a block away by now, running as fast as he could. He hurried after him, knowing it was useless but afraid to let him go like this. Why had he done it, he asked himself, but could get no answer from either his head or his heart. Had there always been something between himself and the boy that neither of them understood? "No," he said to himself. "No, it's your fault. It's always been your fault."

Already the running form of the boy was two blocks ahead of him, and he would soon be out of sight entirely. As he hurried after him he wondered if he would ever be able to draw close to his son again.

Responding

1. Who is the protagonist of the story and what is his goal? Does he fulfill his goal? Why or why not?

2. The exposition and antecedent action (flashback) of this story provide good insights to the source of conflict between father and son. What attitudes and events led to their drifting apart? How accurate is the father in thinking that "He seemed to know less about the boy than anyone?"

3. Why does the son run away from his father? Is he justified in this action? Explain.

4. Do you feel that father and son will ever be reconciled? Discuss, using evidence from the story. If the father had a second chance to relive the evening, is it likely he would do anything differently? Comment.

5. Do you think the title is appropriate? Explain. Is John Purcell a sympathetic character? Why or why not? Does he conform to your mental image of what a father should be like? Why or why not?

6. In your opinion, which is the most powerful episode in the story? Explain how the author uses dialogue and description to make this episode have a dramatic impact.

Student notes, page 242

Mary Peterson

THE CARVED TABLE

Recently remarried, Karen looks at her new husband's family through the eyes of her first husband and finds—an unexpected independence.

I t was her second marriage and Karen sat at the round table in Marblehead with her new family, listening to their conversation and thinking of what her first husband would see, if he was there. He would notice, she thought, my new mother-in-law's enormous diamond, and he would see this new father-in-law's yachting jacket, and he would be disgusted. Might even say, "What are you doing here? You'll lose your soul to these people."

There were six around the table: she and her handsome husband, his parents, and her husband's spoiled-looking older brother and his glossy wife, who tossed her fine red hair and laughed at the right times and made little asides to the mother-in-law while the men held forth. Karen envied that sharing. She envied her thoroughbred sister-in-law who did not take it all so seriously. She herself took it too seriously and she couldn't shake off the feeling that something was terribly wrong.

She touched the carved wood edge of the table with one hand and with the other she reached toward her husband, rested her hand on his knee. He was always quiet during the cocktail hour, but also he listened with an odd, fixed smile: one of complicity— mesmerized like a twelve-year-old trying to learn the hard lessons of being an adult. When you were an adult you drank a lot; you kept up with your father in the drinking. This was difficult, since his father went to the bar for more bourbon often, and with each new drink he grew louder, and with each he had more to say and less that made sense. The man was well-educated, she reminded herself, and certainly he knew much about banking, airplanes, and stocks. But also, he believed children on welfare should be allowed to die, so that we could purify the society. He believed in capital punishment. He believed we should step up the arms race and show more muscle abroad. Wars are different now, she wanted to say. We have nuclear weapons. We need a different set of rules. She did not say these things. Neither did she say that his capitalism created in the minds of the poor a need: they saw the television advertising, they saw the consumption of goods. How could they have any dreams but the ones he himself had? No wonder, she wanted to say, the Cadillac sits outside the tenement, and at the market people buy junk food with food stamps. What do they know about beans and meat? They know what they see on television, in the magazines; they know the Mercedes they see *him* driving. Your capitalism, she wanted to say, is educating them in desperate ignorance. Your free enterprise system.

She did not say any of it.

Her first husband would be thinking and maybe saying these things. He would know that the people around the table were the enemy, the very same she and he had fought when they lived in Chicago and worked against the war in Viet Nam. The same they had studied during the terrible sixties, the one they had hated.

"You're so quiet," her husband said, leaning toward her, giving her his hand. He was handsome and gentle and he didn't pontificate like his father and she loved him in spite of a score of things, and for a hundred others: not the least of them his stability, his good sense, his ability to be socially at ease with people, his open affection with her, the pure security of him.

"I was wondering," she said, "about the carving around this table." She tried to say it quietly, so the others wouldn't hear. "I know one of the wooden scallops was added, because one was broken, and I've been trying to guess if any of these—" and she ran her hand along the perimeter of the table "—is the new one. To see if it really fits so well."

"None have been added," he said. He seemed confused.

"You told me one was new. I remember."

"Karen's right," his father said. "One is new. I can't find it, either."

The other daughter-in-law and the mother had begun to play backgammon. They used an inlaid ebony board and when the dice were thrown they clicked like teeth. Her husband's brother had taken out an expensive cigar and was lighting it with great ceremony. He looked rich. His haircut looked rich and exactly right and his three-piece suit matched his shirt and tie exactly. He had a bored rich face and a sullen lower lip. You could not ask him a question because he would never answer it; he made light of everything.

The mother-in-law was beautiful and smooth-skinned and Karen had often watched her play with her grandchildren. She was the best of the family, but even in the best there was this other thing. In one game, the woman lined the children up to race. When they were ready, she broke away before she'd finished counting—she always won. "Your Grandmother lies," she told the children, laughing. One grandchild cried the first time she did it. The next time, the child who cried—a little girl—broke away early too.

Her first husband would have seen and understood all this, and although she didn't love him and didn't miss him, she respected his intelligence and he was more like her—shared with her a way of seeing. He would have observed her new husband's expensive suit, and her own diamond, and her own good haircut. But he's gone, she thought, and that's over. She released her new husband's hand. I'm seeing with my own eyes, she thought, and I mustn't blame it on anyone else. So now I must decide what to do.

Responding

1. What are the values of Karen's first husband and how are they similar to her own?

2. a) Write a paragraph contrasting the characters and values of Karen's first and second husbands.
   b) In point form make a list of the strengths of the second husband.

3. Discuss the meaning and purpose of the following quotations:
   a) "You'll lose your soul to these people."
   b) "... the people around the table were the enemy..."

4. Why does Karen not say what she is thinking? Discuss her internal conflict.

5. What is the significance of Karen's question about the wooden table scallop? Explain how this episode relates to the story's main conflict.

6. What do you think Karen will finally decide to do? Justify your opinion with references to the text.

7. In groups of three, role-play a chance meeting of Karen, her first husband and her second husband at a restaurant or theatre.

Student notes, page 243

3 CHARACTER

Our experiences in life lead us to meet and get to know many people, some of whom we call acquaintances, and a select few of whom we call good friends. Those we call good friends are usually people we have grown close to over a long period of time. This observation points out one of literature's chief values: reading, particularly reading short stories, gives us easy access to characters we can get to know well simply by turning pages. This involvement with an individual's personality and concerns often makes character stories both enjoyable and thought-provoking. Because these stories provide us with opportunities to grow in awareness and under-standing of ourselves and others, they are usually considered more meaningful than basic, action-oriented stories.

In life, the impressions we form of the people we meet are based mostly on their appearance, what they say, what they do, and what others say about them. In reading, we learn about and judge characters in much the same way; however, writers can give us even more information on which to base our impressions. They can go further than real-life experience by revealing to readers what a character thinks and feels. This advantage allows us to know more personally and immediately the mind of a story's central character. Writers can also give readers a concise summary of what a character is like, providing us with a capsule description so that we may understand the character more quickly than the previously-mentioned methods would allow.

The stories in this unit introduce readers to three rather unusual characters. "Alicia" lets us share the experiences of a young girl as she struggles to understand her older sister's mental illness. "The Parsley Garden" presents the thoughts and feelings of a boy who is intent on regaining the self-respect he lost by being caught shoplift-ing. " Who Said We All Have to Talk Alike " describes the experi-ences of a woman whose views of the world are shaken when she leaves her home community. Each story reveals the fears, joys, beliefs, values, and conflicts of an individual, giving us the opportu-nity to look again at ourselves and people in our own lives.

Gabrielle Roy

ALICIA

There are those like Alicia who live inside themselves. And as Christine learns, nothing—not even a younger sister's love—can overcome some forms of sickness.

I must tell the story of Alicia; certainly it left the greatest mark upon my life; but how dearly it costs me!

Our Alicia with her huge dark blue eyes! And the so-strange contrast in her between those eyes and her coal-black hair! From Maman she had inherited also the loveliest eyebrows I remember ever to have seen, so roundly arched, so high and sharply delineated that they gave her glance an expression of amazement, of pain at the spectacle of life. She was still herself, with her pale, slender face; yet no, it was no longer Alicia. For already she no longer recognized those she so deeply loved; me alone, at times, she still knew. Her strange eyes would come back from so far away that to see them return filled me with dread; then she would look at me, smile at me as before; maybe she would even kiss me in the joy of rediscovering me; but she clung to me too tightly; and of her, of Alicia, I now was frightened! Then she would go back to where she had come from; her eyes would lose us all, relatives, friends, little sister. There would be no one but herself imprisoned within her queer look. Even then I could imagine how terrible it must be to be all alone within oneself.

"Whatever is the matter with Alicia?" I would go ask Maman.

At home we were always very reluctant to cry where anyone could see us. But how very often, at that time, when I went into the kitchen and found Maman alone, I caught her wiping her eyes with the corner of her apron! And she would hastily become a person with a great deal to do, who cannot be bothered. I would insist, "What's the matter with Alicia?"

They—I mean the grownups—were protecting me from the truth. They told me Alicia had nothing the matter with her. Is this what constitutes childhood: by means of lies, to be kept in a world apart? But *they* could not prevent my seeking; and seeking by myself alone, without help, kept bringing me back into their world.

It was summer. A hotter, more brilliant summer I do not think there ever was on Rue Deschambault. We were as though readied for happiness, with our trees full of fruit, flowers all around the house, the lawn well-cropped. If I remember that summer so well, certainly it was because the season was so out of joint, so little in tune with our thoughts. Alicia alone seemed not to be aware of this contrast. She, who was the cause of our misery, withdrew from it as though she had no part in it; almost all the time she was humming.

One day she went up to the attic.

Constantly we would ask each other, worried, as though concerned about a tiny little child who had eluded our watchfulness, "Where is Alicia?"

And almost every day I would find the answer, "In the attic."

Once, though, it took me a long while to discover her. She had hidden herself in the depths of a dark cupboard, and when I at last found her, she was holding her head in her hands; this time she was crying.

Yet how was it that, having found her in an attitude which indicated she wanted to play hide-and-seek with me, I had no feeling that this was a game, nor any taste to join in it? In the past she and I had often played at hiding from each other; yet when we found each other once more, it was to bubble with laughter or accuse each other of cheating.

"Where is Alicia?" Maman would ask me.

And I would tell her; I would say: "Today she's braiding flowers and singing."

Why was it so sad to see Alicia spend hours weaving flowers together to make necklaces and bracelets for her adornment? Merely because she was no longer a little girl? . . .

One day in the attic Alicia put on a long white dress; around her waist she fastened a wide, sky-blue belt; in her hair she tucked some roses. I had never seen her look so lovely; and why was it sad to see her thus? She leaned out of the garret window toward the street and began scattering petals from the roses over the heads of the occasional passers-by. And she sang plaintively, "Here are flowers . . . good people. . . . Here are roses for you who walk by! . . ."

I don't know why, but I felt obliged to go tell Maman that Alicia was throwing roses at the heads of the people in the street; one might have thought it somehow disgraced us.

"Go back up to her; try to distract her," said Maman. "Get her away from the window."

That day, however, Alicia did not even know me. When I tried to make her move, she abruptly gave me a malignant glance and began screaming "Judas! Judas!" at me. I was terribly afraid of Alicia, and ran off trembling. Yet it was only yesterday that Alicia had been taking care of me. She was responsible for me when Maman was very tired or when, wanting a full afternoon undisturbed to tackle some major sewing project, she handed me over to Alicia. She would say, "Alicia, don't you want to take the little one for a walk? Will you look out for her?" Many an older sister would not have enjoyed constantly to be encumbered with a little girl like me. But Alicia never wounded me by seeming to be bored at the prospect of having to look after me.

It's true that I gave her the least possible trouble. We would leave the house together, and I was enchanted at seeing that we always took to the wilder side of the street. Never did we go—Alicia and I —toward town; that did not interest us; we would follow the narrow wooden sidewalk as far as the last house on our street. Then we would continue on across the fields, soon reaching our little grove of black oaks. In my childhood I thought this grove huge; I believed it a forest. . . . I have long realized that it was merely a largish clump of trees none too close together; it could not even wholly hide from us the distant gable of our house. No matter; it was among these small black oaks that I most fully felt the slightly dangerous mystery, the attractions, the solemn joy of being in the woods. Alicia helped me maintain this feeling. She would say to me, as we drew near our little oaks, "See! They look just like conspirators wrapped in their long, black coats." Then we forgot that the oaks were conspirators; we stretched out on the grass and watched the acorns fall, which sometimes landed right on our noses, when we had not been quick enough to dodge them. We could spend hours without exchanging a word. Already Alicia's thoughts, though, were not always happy. One day, having announced to her that when I grew up, I would do fine and beautiful things, Alicia told me sadly, "One says that, and then one never accomplishes anything except paltry things of no account."

"But mine will be great!"

Then, as though I were ill, exposed to I know not what, Alicia took me in her arms; she rocked me under a small oak tree rustling quietly in the wind, and I felt as though I were being cradled by the tree, the sky, by an inexhaustible tenderness. Yet when I pulled myself a little away from Alicia, I saw she was crying.

She told me: "You see, what I should like is that no one suffer. I'd like to spend my life preventing sorrow from touching people— Papa, Maman first of all, and then—oh, everyone. Why not everyone? How much hurt is in the world!"

Whereupon she had again clasped me in her arms, saying "I'll defend you. I won't let them do you harm!"

Now, however, she did not see how miserable we were. She remembered no one of us. She was our greatest unhappiness. When visitors came, we tried to hide her. There were some of our acquaintances and friends who still asked after her; the majority pretended they no longer included her in our number; yet some few still asked Maman, "And your daughter Alicia?"

Maman would explain how Alicia had been stricken with a fever which had, as it were, consumed her, adding what the doctors said of such illnesses: either they killed you or else the sequel was worse than death. . . .

And I would go off into a corner of the garden to ponder her words. Whatever could be worse than death? I suppose I preferred to keep Alicia, unhappy, than to see her die. I was afraid lest now they wanted her dead. And from then on it was I who kept saying, "I'll defend Alicia. I won't let them do her any harm. . . ." But one day she bit me savagely, and Maman noticed it.

She was trembling while she questioned me: "She hurt you? And —before this—has it ever happened that she hurt you?"

I could not wholly deny it; I was filled with bottomless terror.

Then it was that *they* decided to send Alicia away. *They* did not tell me the truth; *they* arranged the truth; *they* wholly transformed it. To all my desperate insistence—"Where is Alicia?"—*they* replied that she was in good hands, that perhaps she would return to health, that I must pray for her. And then, from time to time, I would still ask, "What's the matter with Alicia?"

And Maman, who had been so patient with me, put me off rather harshly. "Don't you see I'm so busy I don't know what I'm about? Leave me alone!" said Maman.

One day Papa and Maman were talking confidentially. I could tell by their faces when what they had to say was of interest to me. I pretended to be busy coloring my picture book. Papa and Maman glanced at me, then continued their conversation.

"It's a chance worth taking," Papa was saying. "Alicia loved her so! . . ."

"But she's only a child! . . . And to take her to such a place. Edouard!" said Maman. "Do you realize? . . ."

But Papa replied, "She was so fond of the baby! The joy of seeing her again, perhaps . . . Shouldn't we try everything?"

"At her age," and Maman indicated me with a motion of her chin, "she could be marked for life. . . ."

Papa insisted, "Remember how she loved her. If anyone can still do anything, it's surely our baby. . . . Only she can work the miracle. . . ."

Then, realizing that they expected a miracle of me, I scuttled off and hid beneath the lower branches of the balsams. They hunted for me all afternoon; and when by evening they had not yet found me, they kept calling from the house, "Petite Misère! Christine!"

Underneath the evergreens in the darkness I was thinking of the picnics we so often had had together—just the two of us, Alicia and I. I presume that she had retained from childhood that need, that deep taste for independence, since we—we children—have so little true independence. In any case, to her as to me, nothing seemed less agreeable, more tiresome, than to sit down at the table for a meal. Thus quite often we persuaded Maman to give us permission to take some bread and jam, which we then consumed—was it not strange?—in a cornfield lying a little beyond the oak grove on the edge of the diminutive Seine River. This spot was not a bit comfortable; it afforded us no least level space on which to spread out our food, and obviously there was no view. Nonetheless, between the high rows of corn, Alicia and I had long taken delight in feeling as though we were closed in, well-protected, wholly hidden. We spent hours there, not in the least embarrassed by the fact that we had just enough room to sit down—to stoop, rather—between the close-planted stalks. The rustling of the big leaves, the occasional cry of a bird in the field, a sound as of rippling water which the wind made as it brushed the young ears, their silk, which we tore off to make ourselves beards or moustaches—to us all this was pleasure and high fun! Moreover—and this gave us a warm feeling of security—no one could possibly have come near us without our hearing them. In the cornfield we were as in a fortress, well-protected against others by the extreme pliancy of the stalks which, by the least change in the tone of their crackling, would have betrayed any invasion of our domain. Maman, however, eventually learned where we spent our afternoons; she had already begun to be anxious.

"In the corn! Why always go eat in the corn when there are such lovely other places?"

Very early in the morning Maman and I left to go there.

On the way I asked, "Have you locked Alicia up?"

Maman tried to laugh. "Locked up! What an idea! Of course not: she's in very good hands. She's being cared for by the best doctors."

But the small town we came to had a dismal look, unlike any other town. At least, so I saw it. Perhaps it was because of me. Since those days I have noticed that our thoughts have a great and curious power over things; on certain days they can make seem beautiful some wretched gray hovel; yet it can also happen that they make very ugly something that is not such in itself. This town seemed to me silent, bored, and somehow ill at ease in the sunlight. On a low hill a little outside the town, there towered a large, high building still more silent and more severe than all the rest; it was to this structure that we bent our steps. But I should mention that on arriving Maman had to ask directions, and she asked with a blush, in a low, unhappy tone. Now that we knew our way, we approached the high brick building and we soon became aware that it was placed in the midst of rather handsome grounds, with paths, seats, even swings, and many trees. But whence came the impression that despite these grounds, this structure had no means of exit anywhere? Maybe because of an iron fence all round it. . . .

I remembered the field of corn; there one was locked in, true enough, but it was a very different thing! . . . Might not freedom reside in remaining within a very tiny space which you can leave if you have a mind to?

And how many trips had I already made with Maman, I thought to myself; some of them the finest in the world, in which I saw everything around me, others so sad they hid from me every vista. How strange is travel!

We knocked on a heavy door. A most impassive woman received us in a parlor. I say parlor for lack of a better word, since it was much better furnished than a convent or priest's house parlor. There was reading matter scattered about, good easy chairs gaily upholstered in chintz. Nevertheless, the idea would not have occurred to me to call this room a living room; you could be there only for the purpose of waiting . . . waiting. . . . Such was the message of its silence; and yet all sorts of tiny sounds reached you from afar, like soft, almost fleeting footsteps, and the noise of keys: keys being turned in locks, keys swinging on a chain tied around the waist. Then I heard a peal of laughter, brief but frightening. I quickly held my hands to my ears. Maman seemed not to have heard it. She did not even notice how greatly I was terrified. Maman must have been deeply saddened no longer even to notice my own sadness. *They* say that sorrow brings people together. This is not always true; that day sorrow built a round wall tight closed about Maman as she sat erect on a straight-backed chair.

Then we heard footsteps coming toward us. The door opened. In the company of a blue-uniformed woman Alicia stood on the threshold. I say Alicia also for want of anything better. For it could not be Alicia who stood that way, her head bent, her body sagging as though broken, broken in I know not what abominable fashion!

And I wanted to cry out to the woman, to the building, to the whole red town, "What have you done to Alicia?"

The woman in uniform told Maman that *she* was much better, that obviously one could not expect too much, but that there was progress; then she left us.

Alicia, having sat down, remained motionless, unseeing.

"Alicia," said Maman, ever so gently, "don't you recognize me?" And Maman named herself: "Your mother . . ." yet so embarrassed at having to say it that, like a wax taper, she seemed to burn and then melt away. . . .

Alicia lifted her head a little; her eyes gave Maman a sideways glance; they swept over Maman's face as though it were that of a pleasant stranger . . . and moved on elsewhere. . . .

It's curious, but only then did I understand the words that, for some time now, Maman occasionally murmured to herself: "In my grave . . . I wish I were in my grave! . . ."

Then she encouraged me with a brief gesture, not over-persuasive, as though she thought, "Do try—you—to work the miracle."

I slipped out of my chair. I moved close to Alicia. I put my arms around her waist, and I, also, called out to her, "Alicia!"

She smiled at me then, but it was like the smile of a small child, who recognizes only very vaguely, by their faces, by their voices, those who love her. And my heart was broken; I know it must have been broken; I had no more courage left for the miracle. I let my head fall over Alicia's knees and I began to cry, suddenly remembering the rustle of the corn leaves above us.

Then I felt Alicia's hands, which softly stroked my wet cheek, as though to take stock of something inexplicable, very strange; and as though this hand were going forth to meet a habit long-forgotten and little by little rediscovered, it began to stroke my temples and my hair.

I turned my head on Alicia's knees. Her eyes were straining, focusing on a problem so absorbing that their pupils betrayed no slightest motion. You would have thought that a light from deep within her was striving to reach her eyes; and that made me think of long dark corridors through which one passes with a lamp in one's hand. . . . Had Alicia, then, so long a distance to traverse, alone in those black corridors? And was it recollection—that tiny glow which from time to time I saw shine behind her eyes?

Abruptly the light shone brighter there. With her small lamp shining in her hand, Alicia must have been nearing the end of the passage; thoughts, real thoughts, flitted across her face, but like veiled, uncertain passengers. Oh, how deeply stirring it is to behold a soul returning to a human countenance!

Alicia held me with her eyes. She looked at me intensely, smiled at me, found my name. She even spoke to me: "The Little One! It's you! Where on earth did you come from all by yourself?"

And then she cried out: "You've come to get me! It's you who have come to get me! . . . I knew you'd come! . . ."

And joy flooded her face as though it were the sun itself. Was it not a thing to marvel at? Returning to life, Alicia's soul first of all found joy! As though the soul had been made for joy! . . .

But at once her lips, her hands began to tremble! Why, immediately after joy, did despair cast itself upon her? Never before had I seen despair, and yet I recognized it. Such it surely was: a moment of lucidity, when you see your life and the harm you do others, all their unhappiness, yet no longer is it possible to change anything about it; it is too late; or else you were yourself only the instrument of suffering. . . . About that, one can do nothing.

This despair did not last long. Neither Maman nor I could have endured it longer . . . nor Alicia herself. It was killing her, as it were, before our very eyes.

For one sole instant, then, we were ourselves within Alicia, and she herself was within us, and we were upon one single shore, close enough to touch, to see one another. . . . Then despair took Alicia away. . . . She began to draw off; and, abruptly, a darksome, invisible stream dug its way between us. Alicia, on the far shore, was moving away . . . mysteriously . . . she withdrew. I yearned to call her, so far gone was she already. And she, like someone about to disappear—she raised her hand and waved it toward us.

After this she seemed like a well-behaved little girl of about my age who toys with her fingers, crossing and then uncrossing them.

She died a few months later. *They* buried her, as one buries everybody, whether a person has died on the day of his death—or long before, because, maybe, of life itself. . . . What difference can there be here? . . . And why did they say of Alicia that God . . . when He came to take her . . . had shown her a mercy? . . .

Responding

1. What seems to have caused Alicia's illness? Did Christine, as a child, understand her sister's problem? Comment.

2. What do the parents hope will happen when they bring Christine to visit Alicia? How does Christine react during the visit?

3. Christine, the story's narrator, is an adult looking back on specific events in her childhood. What advantage is gained by having Christine tell the story as an adult rather than as a child?

4. What does the story reveal about Christine's personality? Does the experience with Alicia change Christine at all? Explain.

5. What might the story have gained or lost by being told through the eyes of Alicia's mother?

6. Write the dialogue for the conversation Christine might have had with her parents, discussing Alicia's illness at the beginning of the story.

7. Most people are able to cope with the world, while some, such as Alicia, have great difficulty handling the stresses of life. What, in your view, are some qualities that help people cope with problems and responsibilities?

Student notes, page 244.

William Saroyan

THE PARSLEY GARDEN

Humiliated at being caught shoplifting, an intense young boy seeks revenge—on his own terms.

O ne day in August Al Condraj was wandering through Woolworth's without a penny to spend when he saw a small hammer that was not a toy but a real hammer and he was possessed with a longing to have it. He believed it was just what he needed by which to break the monotony and with which to make something. He had gathered some first-class nails from Foley's Packing House where the boxmakers worked and where they had carelessly dropped at least fifteen cents' worth. He had gladly gone to the trouble of gathering them together because it had seemed to him that a nail, as such, was not something to be wasted. He had the nails, perhaps a half pound of them, at least two hundred of them, in a paper bag in the apple box in which he kept his junk at home.

Now, with the ten-cent hammer he believed he could make something out of box wood and the nails, although he had no idea what. Some sort of a table perhaps, or a small bench.

At any rate he took the hammer and slipped it into the pocket of his overalls, but just as he did so a man took him firmly by the arm without a word and pushed him to the back of the store into a small office. Another man, an older one, was seated behind a desk in the

71

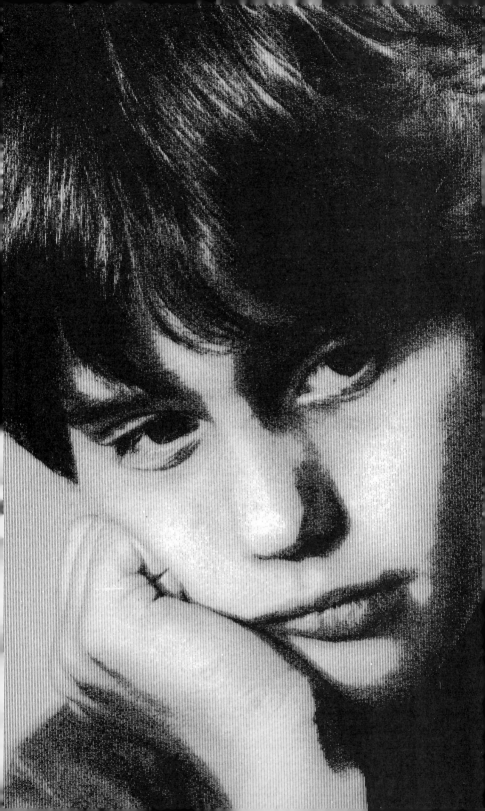

office, working with papers. The younger man, the one who had captured him, was excited and his forehead was covered with sweat.

"Well," he said, "here's one more of them."

The man behind the desk got to his feet and looked Al Condraj up and down.

"What's *he* swiped?"

"A hammer." The young man looked at Al with hatred. "Hand it over," he said.

The boy brought the hammer out of his pocket and handed it to the young man, who said, "I ought to hit you over the head with it, that's what I ought to do."

He turned to the older man, the boss, the manager of the store, and he said, "What do you want me to do with him?"

"Leave him with me," the older man said.

The younger man stepped out of the office, and the older man sat down and went back to work. Al Condraj stood in the office fifteen minutes before the older man looked at him again.

"Well," he said.

Al didn't know what to say, the man wasn't looking at him, he was looking at the door.

Finally Al said, "I didn't mean to steal it. I just need it and I haven't got any money."

"Just because you haven't got any money doesn't mean you've got a right to steal things," the man said. "Now, does it?"

"No, sir."

"Well, what am I going to do with you? Turn you over to the police?"

Al didn't say anything, but he certainly didn't want to be turned over to the police. He hated the man, but at the same time he realized somebody else could be a lot tougher than he was being.

"If I let you go, will you promise never to steal from this store again?"

"Yes, sir."

"All right," the man said. "Go out this way and don't come back to this store until you've got some money to spend."

He opened a door to the hall that led to the alley, and Al Condraj hurried down the hall and out into the alley.

The first thing he did when he was free was laugh, but he knew he had been humiliated, and he was deeply ashamed. It was not in his nature to take things that did not belong to him. He hated the young man who had caught him and he hated the manager of the store who had made him stand in silence in the office so long. He hadn't liked it at all when the young man had said he ought to hit him over the head with the hammer.

He should have had the courage to look him straight in the eye and say, "You and who else?"

Of course he *had* stolen the hammer and he had been caught, but it seemed to him he oughtn't to have been so humiliated.

After he had walked three blocks he decided he didn't want to go home just yet, so he turned around and started walking back to town. He almost believed he meant to go back and say something to the young man who had caught him. And then he wasn't sure he didn't mean to go back and steal the hammer again, and this time *not* get caught. As long as he had been made to feel like a thief anyway, the least he ought to get out of it was the hammer.

Outside the store he lost his nerve, though. He stood in the street, looking in, for at least ten minutes.

Then, crushed and confused and now bitterly ashamed of himself, first for having stolen something, then for having been caught, then for having been humiliated, then for not having guts enough to go back and do the job right, he began walking home again, his mind so troubled that he didn't greet his pal Pete Wawchek when they came face to face outside Graf's Hardware.

When he got home he was too ashamed to go inside and examine his junk, so he had a long drink of water from the faucet in the back yard. The faucet was used by his mother to water the stuff she planted every year: okra, bell peppers, tomatoes, cucumbers, onions, garlic, mint, eggplants and parsley.

His mother called the whole business the parsley garden, and every night in the summer she would bring chairs out of the house and put them around the table she had had Ondro, the neighborhood handyman, make for her for fifteen cents, and she would sit at the table and enjoy the cool of the garden and the smell of the things she had planted and tended.

Sometimes she would even make a salad and moisten the flat old-country bread and slice some white cheese, and she and he would have supper in the parsley garden. After supper she would attach the water hose to the faucet and water her plants and the place would be cooler than ever and it would smell real good, real fresh and cool and green, all the different growing things making a green-garden smell out of themselves and the air and the water.

After the long drink of water he sat down where the parsley itself was growing and he pulled a handful of it out and slowly ate it. Then he went inside and told his mother what had happened. He even told her what he had *thought* of doing after he had been turned loose: to go back and steal the hammer again.

"I don't want you to steal," his mother said in broken English. "Here is ten cents. You go back to that man and you give him this money and you bring it home, that hammer."

"No," Al Condraj said. "I won't take your money for something I don't really need. I just thought I ought to have a hammer, so I could make something if I felt like it. I've got a lot of nails and some box wood, but I haven't got a hammer."

"Go buy it, that hammer," his mother said.

"No," Al said.

"All right," his mother said. "Shut up."

That's what she always said when she didn't know what else to say.

Al went out and sat on the steps. His humiliation was beginning to really hurt now. He decided to wander off along the railroad tracks to Foley's because he needed to think about it some more. At Foley's he watched Johnny Gale nailing boxes for ten minutes, but Johnny was too busy to notice him or talk to him, although one day at Sunday school, two or three years ago, Johnny had greeted him and said, "How's the boy?" Johnny worked with a boxmaker's hatchet and everybody in Fresno said he was the fastest boxmaker in town. He was the closest thing to a machine any packing house ever saw. Foley himself was proud of Johnny Gale.

Al Condraj finally set out for home because he didn't want to get in the way. He didn't want somebody working hard to notice that he was being watched and maybe say to him, "Go on, beat it." He didn't want Johnny Gale to do something like that. He didn't want to invite another humiliation.

On the way home he looked for money but all he found was the usual pieces of broken glass and rusty nails, the things that were always cutting his bare feet every summer.

When he got home his mother had made a salad and set the table, so he sat down to eat, but when he put the food in his mouth he just didn't care for it. He got up and went into the three-room house and got his apple box out of the corner of his room and went through his junk. It was all there, the same as yesterday.

He wandered off back to town and stood in front of the closed store, hating the young man who had caught him, and then he went along to the Hippodrome and looked at the display photographs from the two movies that were being shown that day.

Then he went along to the public library to have a look at all the books again, but he didn't like any of them, so he wandered around town some more, and then around half-past eight he went home and went to bed.

His mother had already gone to bed because she had to be up at five to go to work at Inderrieden's, packing figs. Some days there would be work all day, some days there would be only half a day of it, but whatever his mother earned during the summer had to keep them the whole year.

He didn't sleep much that night because he couldn't get over what had happened, and he went over six or seven ways by which to adjust the matter. He went so far as to believe it would be necessary to kill the young man who had caught him. He also believed it would be necessary for him to steal systematically and successfully the rest of his life. It was a hot night and he couldn't sleep.

Finally, his mother got up and walked barefooted to the kitchen for a drink of water and on the way back she said to him softly, "Shut up."

When she got up at five in the morning he was out of the house, but that had happened many times before. He was a restless boy, and he kept moving all the time every summer. He was making mistakes and paying for them, and he had just tried stealing and had been caught at it and he was troubled. She fixed her breakfast, packed her lunch and hurried off to work, hoping it would be a full day.

It was a full day, and then there was overtime, and although she had no more lunch she decided to work on for the extra money, anyway. Almost all the other packers were staying on, too, and her neighbor across the alley, Leeza Ahboot, who worked beside her, said, "Let us work until the work stops, then we'll go home and fix a supper between us and eat it in your parsley garden where it's so cool. It's a hot day and there's no sense not making an extra fifty or sixty cents."

When the two women reached the garden it was almost nine o'clock, but still daylight, and she saw her son nailing pieces of box wood together, making something with a hammer. It looked like a bench. He had already watered the garden and tidied up the rest of the yard, and the place seemed very nice, and her son seemed very serious and busy. She and Leeza went straight to work for their supper, picking bell peppers and tomatoes and cucumbers and a great deal of parsley for the salad.

Then Leeza went to her house for some bread which she had baked the night before, and some white cheese, and in a few minutes they were having supper together and talking pleasantly about the successful day they had had. After supper, they made Turkish coffee over an open fire in the yard. They drank the coffee and smoked a cigarette apiece, and told one another stories about their experiences in the old country and here in Fresno, and then they looked into their cups at the grounds to see if any good fortune was indicated, and there was: health and work and supper out of doors in the summer and enough money for the rest of the year.

Al Condraj worked and overheard some of the things they said, and then Leeza went home to go to bed, and his mother said, "Where you get it, that hammer, Al?"

"I got it at the store."

"How you get it? You steal it?"

Al Condraj finished the bench and sat on it. "No," he said. "I didn't steal it."

"How you get it?"

"I worked at the store for it," Al said.

"The store where you steal it yesterday?"

"Yes."

"Who give you job?"

"The boss."

"What you do?"

"I carried different stuff to the different counters."

"Well, that's good," the woman said. "How long you work for that little hammer?"

"I worked all day," Al said. "Mr. Clemmer gave me the hammer after I'd worked one hour, but I went right on working. The fellow who caught me yesterday showed me what to do, and we worked together. We didn't talk, but at the end of the day he took me to Mr. Clemmer's office and he told Mr. Clemmer that I'd worked hard all day and ought to be paid at least a dollar."

"That's good," the woman said.

"So Mr. Clemmer put a silver dollar on his desk for me, and then the fellow who caught me yesterday told him the store needed a boy like me every day, for a dollar a day, and Mr. Clemmer said I could have the job."

"That's good," the woman said. "You can make it a little money for yourself."

"I left the dollar on Mr. Clemmer's desk," Al Condraj said, "and I told them both I didn't want the job."

"Why you say that?" the woman said. "Dollar a day for eleven-year-old boy good money. Why you not take job?"

"Because I hate the both of them," the boy said. "I would never work for people like that. I just looked at them and picked up my hammer and walked out. I came home and I made this bench."

"All right," his mother said. "Shut up."

His mother went inside and went to bed, but Al Condraj sat on the bench he had made and smelled the parsley garden and didn't feel humiliated any more.

But nothing could stop him from hating the two men, even though he knew they hadn't done anything they shouldn't have done.

Responding

1. What circumstances motivate Al to steal the hammer?

2. Describe the different emotions Al feels from the moment he is caught to the point where he tells his mother about the incident. What bothers him most about the whole experience?

3. What actions does Al consider as he struggles with his painful emotions? What do these thoughts reveal about his character? What does his final action tell us about him?

4. Describe Al's home life. Does his mother seem, in your view, a responsible parent? Why or why not?

5. Al's story is mainly about losing one's self-respect and then regaining it. What happens to people sometimes when they lose their self-respect? How might these people be helped to regain their self-respect?

6. Write a story or tell an anecdote you know about shoplifting.

Student notes, page 244

Wilma Elizabeth McDaniel

WHO SAID WE ALL HAVE TO TALK ALIKE

True, she "talked different," but who would have guessed that the kind-hearted Neffie could be such a bad influence on the two young girls? Certainly not Neffie.

Who knows how Neffie Pike's speech pattern was formed? Her Ozark family had talked the same way for generations. They added an "r" to many words that did not contain that letter. In spite of this, or because of it, their speech was clear and colorful and to the point. Most people understood what they were talking about, exactly.

Neffie was her parents' daughter. She called a toilet, "torelet," and a woman, "worman," very comfortably. The teacher at the country school never attempted to change Neffie's manner of speaking. She said that Neffie had a fine imagination and should never allow anyone to squelch it. In fact, Neffie never really knew that she talked different from most other people.

People in the tiny community of Snowball really loved Neffie. She was a good neighbor, unfailingly cheerful and helpful. The appearance of her tall and bony figure at the door of a sickroom or a bereaved family meant comfort and succor. A great woman, everyone in Snowball agreed.

She would have probably lived her life out in the same lumber house if her husband had not died. In the months that followed his death she developed a restless feeling. Home chores, church and charity work did not seem to be enough to occupy her mind. She started to read big-town newspapers at the library in nearby Marshall, something new for her. She became especially interested in the out-of-state employment want ads. She mentioned to neighbors, "They are a lot of good jobs out there in the world."

One day she came home from Marshall and stopped at old Grandma Meade's house. She sat down in a canebottom chair and announced, "I have got me a job in California. I am a selling my house and lot to a couple of retired people from Little Rock. They will be moving in the first of June."

Grandma Meade sat in shocked silence for several seconds, then said, "Honey, I do not believe it. I mean that I never in the world imagined that you would consider leaving Snowball. You and Lollis was so happy together here." Her voice trailed off, "Of course nobody could foretell the Lord would call him so young."

Neffie looked stonily at her and said with her usual clarity, "A widder worman is a free worman, especially if she don't have no children. She ought to be free to come and go like she pleases. After all, I am only fifty-one years old. I can do as much work as I ever did. This job is taking care of two little girls while their mother works at some high-paying job. She has already sent me a bus ticket. I wouid be a fool not to go. Everyone has been to California except me. I always hankered to see the state for myself. Now is my chance to see some of the rest of the world. It may sound foolish, but it will sort of be like having a dorter of my own and grandchildren. I aim to write you a long letter when I get settled down out there."

Neffie left for California on schedule. After two weeks Grandma Meade began to worry a bit. She said, "I thought that Neffie surely would have dropped us a line by now. The last thing she told me was that she would write me a long letter. Well, maybe she hasn't got settled down yet."

A month passed without any word from Neffie.

Bug Harrison was at Grandma Meade's house when Neffie returned the day after Snowball's big Fourth of July celebration.

Neffie put her suitcases down and began at the beginning. "Grandma, you was so right about so many things. I knowed I was in trouble hock-deep, only one minute after I stepped off that bus in California. A purty young worman come forward to meet me and said she was Beryl. I busted out and told her, 'My, you are a purty

worman, even purtier than your pitcher.' She kinda shrunk back
and looked at me like I had used a cussword. She stood there
holding her little girls' hands and asked me, where on earth did you
hear a word like worman, was it a female worm of some kind? She
said, 'Worman is woe-man,' like you say woh to a horse.

"Her remark nearly knocked me off my feet. I felt like a fool, and
I didn't even know why. My stomach started churning. I durst not
say anything to defend myself, because I hadn't done anything
wrong.

"We started walking to Beryl's station wagon in the parking lot. I
told her that I never was blessed with a dorter or son, either. That
set her off again. She said that her children were at a very impressionable age, that I would have to watch my speech and learn the
correct pronunciation of words. She did not want them picking up
incorrect speech patterns and something she called coll-oke-ism,
something I had, and didn't even realize. I decided to shut up and
get in the car. The worman had already paid for my fare. I felt that
I had to at least give her a few months' service, if I could stand the
punishment at all.

"On our way to Beryl's house, she stopped at a drive-in restaurant and ordered cheeseburgers and milkshakes for all of us. I
decided to just eat and listen.

"It was sure a pleasurable drive on to Beryl's home. We followed
the same county highway for the entire seven miles. The road was
lined on both sides with pams, tall with them fronds waving in the
breeze. It reminded me of pitchers I have seen of The Holy Land,
really touched my heart. I forgot myself again and said that I never
had seen pams before except in pitchers. Quick as a flash Beryl told
me, 'They are pall-ms, not pams. There is an l in the word.' After
that, I sure buttoned up my mouth. I just said yes or no to anything
she asked me.

"Her house turned out to be a real nice place, bright and modern
with every type of electrical gadget you could think of. There were
four bedrooms, each with a bath. I was so tired and upset over
Beryl's attitude that I begged off sitting up to visit with her and the
little girls. I ran me a full tub of warm water and took me a long
soaking bath. I fell into bed and went sound asleep. Worman, I
plumb died away, slept all night without waking up. To show you
how hard I slept, there was a fairly severe earthquake in the central

part of California where Beryl lived. It even shook a few things off a living room shelf. I tell you, I wouldn't have heard Gabriel blow his horn that night.

"I woke up feeling relieved that it was Monday. Beryl left for work promptly at seven-thirty. That meant the girls and I had the house to ourselves. Worman, I am a telling you, they was two living dolls, Pat and Penny. I made them bran muffins for breakfast and scrambled some eggs. They ate until they nearly foundered. It seemed like they had never seen a bran muffin before, asked me if I would cook them the same thing each day.

"I told them I knew how to cook other good old homely dishes, too. Every day, I tried something new on them, biscuits and sausage and milk gravy, buttermilk pancakes, waffles, popovers, french toast, corn dodgers, fried mush. You name it, worman, I cooked it for those dolls. It wouldn't be no big deal for the kids here in Snowball, they was raised to eat like that, but it was hog heaven to Pat and Penny."

Grandma Meade had been listening intently, her eyes pinned on Neffie's face. Now she asked, "How did Beryl like your cooking?"

Neffie laughed heartily. She said, "To put it plain, she LOVED it. I can say that she never found any flaw in my cooking, only made one complaint connected with it. I boirled her a fine big cabbage and hamhock dinner and made cornbread for our supper one evening. When we started to sit down at the table, I said that it was a nice change to have a boirled dinner now and then. That set her off like a firecracker. She said, 'That is boil-ed, not boirled.' I decided to let that snide remark pass. I saw she started dishing up the food—she lit in on it like a starving hounddog. That showed what she thought of my cooking, didn't it? My cooking sure helped me get through them weeks as good as I did."

Bug Harrison broke in, "What were your duties during the day?"

Neffie said, "I was hired to take care of the two little girls. That is what I done. I cooked because people have to eat. I always have, always will. That didn't put no extra strain on me. The girls and I played the most of the day. They would sit on each arm of my chair and listen to me tell them about my life back in Arkansas. I didn't hold back nothing. I told them about haunted houses, ghosts, robbers, bank holdups, tornadoes, snakes, tarantulas, times when the river flooded and we had to float on a rooftop to save our lives. Lordy, worman, they just ate it up. They would listen to me with their eyes as big as saucers. I don't quite know why I done it, but I asked the girls not to tell their mother about my stories. They were as secretive as little private detectives until a week ago. They got so excited over one of my stories that they forgot theirselves. I was busy in the kitchen putting some homemade noodles into a pot of chicken broth. I heard Pat tell her mother, 'Mom, back in Arkansas where Neffie used to live, they are wormans that can tell fortunes for people. They can look right through your face and tell if you are telling the truth or a lie. They can rub your warts with skunk oirl and say some words and all the warts will fall off, never ever come back.' I figured I was in bad trouble, but I kept on dropping the noodles into the broth. I was a hundred percent right about the trouble.

"Beryl blowed her stack. She marched right back to the kitchen with the girls at her heels. She stood in the door and said, 'I have been afraid of this very thing. Neffie, I just can't keep you on any longer.'

"At that point Pat and Penny throwed themselves down on the floor and started bawling like two young calves. Pat sobbed out real angry-like, 'Yes, you CAN keep Neffie! She is the best storyteller in the whole world and the best cooker. If she goes home to Arkansas, we won't never have no more biscuits and sausage and gravy.' The tears began to run down her little face.

"Beryl stood there with her face like a flintrock. It looked like she wanted to be nice to me, but that her duty come first with her. She drawed in her breath and said, 'Neffie, you are as good and kind and honest as you can be, exceptional, but your speech is totally unacceptable. My children are at a very impressionable age. I have tried to overlook it, but they are definitely being influenced in the wrong direction. They say dorter and orter with regularity. This pattern must be eradicated immediately. I shall be happy to pay your travelling expenses home. You can look on this trip out West as my vacation gift to you.' I could see that her mind was made up and she wasn't going to change it.

"I did think to ask her if she had some other babysitter in mind. I didn't want to run out and leave her in a bind without one. She said there was a young girl from the college who wanted day work, so she could attend night classes. She thought that would work out great. I got her point. The college girl would be different from me, more to suit Beryl.

"Well, to shorten my story, she bought me a big box of real expensive chocolates and put me on the bus with my paid ticket, just like she had promised. She and the girls stood there beside the bus waiting for it to pull out. Penny looked up at me and blew me a kiss. I heard her say as plain as plain could be, 'Neffie, you are a sweet worman.' Then I saw Beryl put her hand over Penny's mouth. Right then, the bus pulled out of the depot and I lost sight of them.

"Worman, I done a lot of thinking as that bus rolled along the highway. I would eat a chocolate and think over my experience with Beryl. Things kind of cleared up in my mind, like having blinders taken off of my eyes. I saw I had really been ignorant of some things that other folks knowed. I didn't talk right to suit some of them, but that wasn't my fault. *I didn't know we was all supposed to talk the same way.* I thought people hadn't all talked the same since before God tore down their tower at Babel and confused all their tongues. Folks all over the world have talked different ever since then. I guess some of them like Beryl want to go back to pre-Babel days. Anyway, it was sure an eye-opener to me, hurt me, too. Beryl just plain separated herself from me. It was like she took a sharp knife and cut a melon in half, and throwed away the half that was me. You know what you do with a piece of melon you don't want. You throw it with the rinds into the garbage can. Worman, who said that we all have to talk alike? Can anyone tell me that?"

Responding

1. Describe the way in which Neffie Pike is viewed by (a) her community, (b) Beryl, and (c) Pat and Penny.

2. Describe the differences in the values held by Neffie and Beryl. Was there any solution to their problem in living together in one household? Comment.

3. At the end of the story, what are Neffie's feelings about her experience? How might Neffie's friends have answered her final question?

4. What does the story have to say about valuing other human beings?

5. In this story we see a division over the issue of correctness in speech. What are some other issues over which people become divided in relationships? How might such gaps be closed?

6. Is Neffie right when she maintains that differences in speech are unimportant? Give reasons for your views.

Student notes, page 245

4 SETTING AND ATMOSPHERE

Many of us, when we tell stories, start with where and when the events took place. The opening may be relatively factual: "Yesterday, when I was on my way home from school, I stopped at the store across the street from the park." Or the start may be dramatic: "It was just after midnight and no other sounds could be heard except my own footsteps as I hurried down the dark alley." Either way, when we tell a story, we need to help our listeners picture the events by giving them an idea of the time and the place of the story.

Our own stories—and we each have many based on personal experiences—are set in a variety of locations and time periods. These details may be, simply, nothing more than the place and time. However, we know—if we have ever struggled against elements of the environment, such as cold, heat, or turbulent water—that the setting itself can be the source of the conflict and the main reason for the story.

Finally, setting is important because it helps to create the atmosphere of a story. We have only to recall a time when we walked home late at night and felt nervous as we passed dark entranceways and listened to the wind rustling in nearby bushes—or *was* it the wind? The place and time work together to cause that nervousness. In the same way, the setting of a story can stir in readers an emotional reaction that makes the story more meaningful.

The stories that follow offer three very different experiences with setting and atmosphere. The first, "A Mountain Journey," presents a life-and-death conflict in a hostile environment; the second, "The Veldt," combines a futuristic setting with a sinister atmosphere; and the third, "The Wish," presents a simple setting as the background for a shocking series of events. These three stories help us to see the significance of setting and atmosphere in relation to the events of the story.

Howard O'Hagan

A MOUNTAIN JOURNEY

Trapper Dave Conroy has travelled far and is alone in the winter wilderness.
Though "bushed", he presses on toward safety, driven by a gnawing fear of
death . . .

D ave Conroy, whose breath had hung stubby icicles on his
moustache, paused upon the very summit of the pass. He
tucked his ski poles under his arms, leaned upon them, sinking their
discs into the creaking snow, and while he rested there panting, the
cold was an old man's fingers feeling craftily through his clothes.

He was tired. He was so tired that his mouth was dry with the
taste of salt. He was more tired than he had any right to be, and
Hoodoo cabin on Hoodoo creek, where he could pass the night, was
still five miles away. It was downhill now though, downhill all the
way. For the first time during the long day he could stand back on
his skis and let them carry him where he wished to go. Since
daylight he had come twenty miles and climbed four thousand feet
from the lower Smokey to the pass. On his shoulders he had lifted
upwards with him at every step his pack of food for another five
days on the trail, his blankets, axe and fifty pounds of fur for the
market—the result of six weeks' trapping on the head of the Jackpine. At every step too, he had broken trail and his skis had sunk a
foot in the new snow, white and soft as flour.

He knew as he stood on the summit that he should have made
camp two miles back in the timber and crossed the divide in the
morning. Back there he had passed a fine spruce tree, its wide

branches sweeping low, so that close against its trunk, cradled in its roots, he had seen the brown mossy ground where no snow had fallen and where he might have made his fire and spread his blankets. That tree, like a strong and lonely woman, called to his weary body to stop. But two hours of daylight remained and he went on.

He thought that if he had waited another two weeks to come out, till March, the snow would have had a crust for travelling, the days would have been longer, the cold less severe. Anyway, a man was a fool to travel alone in the mountains, especially with a heavy pack, bucking a fresh fall of snow. A man when he was alone would travel too far. He would travel till he could travel no more, for the mere sake of travelling, when a day or two's delay in the time of his arrival made no difference at all.

Still, the worst was over. It was downgrade now to the railroad, eighty miles of trail along the Snake Indian River with cabins to put up at every night. No more siwashing under trees, burrowing four feet down in the snow for a place to sleep, with a snow-covered tree sweating in the heat of his fire, dripping water on his neck and dampening his blankets. Not that under such conditions a man slept very much. It was too cold. If he slept, his fire slept with him. It was better to stay awake, his blankets over his shoulders, and a pile of wood handy at his elbow.

Up there on the pass it was very still. No wind blew and his breath rose white and yellow before him. His heart thumped and hissed in his breast, and the silence about him as he listened became a roar as if it were the roar of the grey earth rolling on through space and time. Behind him his ski trail stretched a few feet, two black lines with the webbed marks of his ski poles pacing beside them. Mist, like the shadow of universal darkness on the treeless summit, moved about him, searched every crevice of the mountain land, roamed in great billows, formed in the blindness and suffering of eternal homelessness.

Conroy turned his skis down the slope before him. He was beginning to feel like a ghost on an abandoned planet and he wanted to see the works of man about him once again. He longed for the sight of a cabin, a clearing in the forest, yellow flaming blazes on trees beside the trail. Snow, flung up by the prow of his skis, pattered lightly against his thighs and as he hummed downwards he thought of supper—brown curled bacon, brown bannock, rice with butter melting on it, tea red and strong as rum.

The rolling alplands, a white sea frozen into weary immobility, became a broken parkland and he made long sweeping turns around clumps of spruce and balsam. Dark green trees came out of the thinning mist towards him, touched him with outflung branches, passed in a flutter and flurry of snow-dust. The cold wind against his face, the loud wind howling in crescendo by his ears, the flow of wind that pressed his trousers tight against his legs, gave him back strength as he exulted in the rush of his descent. Tears smarted in his eyes and through them he saw the landscape opaque and blurred as though it were vibrating to the speed of his passage.

He swung to the right in a wide telemark that threw snow in his face, swept down an open meadowland where the black tips of willows showed between two walls of timber, dropped off a cutbank to the frozen river, glanced a moment over his shoulder at the curved beauty of his ski trail on the hill above, curved and smooth and thin, like the tracing of a pen upon the snow.

And as he looked back, while still sliding forward with the momentum of his descent, the ice broke beneath him. It broke with a low muffled reverberation, startling as if the river had spoken. The snow rifted about him, the points of his skis dropped down. He was thrown forward and to save himself from falling on his face plunged down his hands. His pack slipped forward upon the back of his head and held him. The river was shallow and his hands rested on its gravelled bottom. He saw the snow melt around his wrists and flow into the top of his mittens, searing the flesh of his wrists like flame. He saw dark water streaming in furrows by his wrists and before he staggered upright again heard water tinkling over pebbles, murmuring, protesting, running downhill between ice and pebbles to the Arctic Ocean.

Conroy was too weak to rise beneath the pack. He rolled over upon his side, slipped the thongs of the ski poles from his wrists, dropped his pack on the snow beside him, raised himself and lifted his skis from the water. Water had seeped down his socks into his boots and his feet were cold and clammy.

He had fallen into an air hole. Probably a warm spring entered into the river nearby and above it the ice was thin. That was a peril of winter travel. But the rivers, levelled with ice and snow, were the winter highways of the mountains, and a man, when he could, travelled along them in preference to breaking a heavy trail in the timber.

Conroy unclamped his skis, upended them, and stood knee-deep in the snow. Already the water on them had crusted into ice. He took off his sodden mit ens, opened his clasp-knife, and tried to scrape the ice from the skis' running surface. He knew what he should do. He should stop, make a fire, dry his hands and feet, change his socks and mittens. But it was late. It would mean siwashing for another night underneath a tree. A biting wind was driving the mist back up the valley and the sun westering behind the ranges threw long feeble shadows across the snow. He was less than three miles from the cabin, and the promise of its warmth and comfort would not let him stop.

He wriggled his toes in his boots. They were cold, but perhaps, he thought, not wet. Only his ankles and heels seemed wet. If he hurried he could make it. He slammed his right foot back into his ski iron, bent down to clamp it to his ski, but his fingers already were numbed with the cold. He rose again, thrashed his arms about his shoulders, bringing the blood tingling to their tips, opened his pack sack and found a pair of woollen inner mitts. He would have to get along without the moose-hide outers. They were already frozen stiff and he put them into his pack.

His skis clamped to his feet at last, he hoisted his pack, took his poles and started off, hunching his toes to keep the circulation going. Ice on the bottom of the skis dragged heavily in the snow, but he fought against it, pushing on his poles, knowing that speed was his one means of escape from the cold hand of wilderness that pressed against his back.

The long white avenue of the river opened before him, lined on either side by tall spruce trees. The wind was rising with the sundown. It whipped snow against his face, cut through the weave of his woollen mitts, set the forest moaning beside him. He bent his head against it, his eyes on the black tapering points of his skis, ducking and dodging through the snow. It was as though he were engaged in some fantastic pursuit with those ski points always just beyond him, their tight cheeks pulled back into a cadaverous grin.

His shoulder muscles, as he lunged against the ski poles, bulged as though they would burst their skin, ached until their pain became a cry within him. His legs moving back and forth beneath him seemed tireless. They could go on forever and he no longer knew whether he could stop them. The pain in his shoulders was the only reality of his existence and his body was no more than the shape of agony and effort crawling through the twilight, across the long shadows of spruce trees laid upon the snow.

He came up from the river through the timber into the cabin clearing. But no log walls rose to greet him. No closed door waited for his touch to open. He stood in the middle of the clearing where the cabin had been, hemmed about by swaying pine trees, pine trees that swayed as the wind sighed through them. Snow, as if it had garnered light from the day, cast upwards a shadowless glow and Conroy saw close to him the black butts of congregated logs, a corner of the cabin, draped in white, rising lonely as a monument left by men a hundred years ago.

Since he had passed that way, fire had gutted the cabin. A few log ends remained above ground. It was as though the cabin had subsided into the snow that rose like a slow inundation to cover it. A beggared moon from behind a grey rack of clouds wandered in the sky above the earth's desolation and in its light he perceived on the slope above him, where the fire had leaped from the cabin, stiff, branchless trees, like a parade of skeletons climbing up the mountainside.

The next cabin was at Blue Creek, eighteen miles down the river. It was farther than he had strength to go. He would camp here in the clearing where the cabin had been burned. He slipped his pack off and reached toward it for the handle of his axe to cut kindling, making shavings for his fire. His fingers refused to bend. Protected only by the woollen mitts, they were stiff with the cold. He beat his hands about his shoulders, flung his arms in circles, took off his mittens and rubbed his hands together in the snow, but felt no blood pulsing in his fingertips.

He bit his fingers. They were cold and white and unresponsive as a dead man's. His right thumb tingled; when he rubbed his hands across his face, his beard bristled on the palms. It was only his fingers that defied him. He had been a fool. He should have made a fire when he fell through the ice, and should have spent the night three miles up the river under a tree. He had always said that mountain travel was not dangerous if a man knew how to take care of himself. Any man who froze his hands or feet had only himself to blame . . .

As he stood there, stamping on his skis, his arms flapping at his sides, he remembered Duncan Macdonald, who trapped in the Beaver River country and who had walked thirty miles to the railroad on frozen feet to have them amputated by the doctor. Because he could trap no more, Macdonald had opened a cobbler's shop in Jasper to make boots he could no longer wear himself, and Conroy saw him now at his bench, laughing, not saying anything at all, just laughing, his red face wrinkled as he nodded his heavy bald head and laughed.

Conroy decided that his hands were not frozen, his feet, which he could not longer feel in his boots, not frozen. They were only numb. He needed fire to warm them. Since he could not make kindling, since he could not bend his fingers around the shaft of his axe, he would set a tree afire, he would set the forest in a blaze around him and warm himself in its midst. Small dry twigs under a spruce tree would flame like paper. Putting his left wrist over his right, he forced his right hand into the pocket where he carried his match-safe. He pried it out and it fell into the snow at his feet. He spread his skis and leaned down to pick it up. He poked his hands into the snow. They were like two sticks of wood on the ends of his arms and shoved the safe deeper and farther from him. He stooped lower still and finally, pressing it between his wrists, filched it out. He held it there before him, at arm's length, a round tin cylinder that contained the red flame and blustering smoke of fire. His right thumb, still moving to his command, pressed it into his palm, but his fingers would not catch it, would not twist it open. They would not bring the match-safe to him. They held it from him. If they would only bend, those fingers. If they would understand when he spoke to them.

He looked about him as if he would find the realities of his situation in the snow at his feet. He was eighty miles from the railroad, a journey of four days. Unable to light a fire, without warmth or food, he would never make it. His fingers were frozen. His feet probably were frozen too. He had one chance. Across the river from Hoodoo Creek where he stood, a high pass led over into the Moose River. Frank MacMoran trapped up there and had his cabin on Terrace Creek. From Hoodoo Creek to Terrace Creek was no more than ten miles. If he left his pack behind, he could probably pull through. He had never finished a day in the mountains yet without another ten miles up his sleeve.

His back was wet with sweat from carrying the pack, and he shivered with the cold. The cold was nibbling at him, at his nose, at his cheeks, crawling like a wet thing across his back. He forced his hands into his mittens, shoved them through the thongs of his ski poles and started off. He did not need to grasp the poles tightly. His hands rested upon the thongs which bore the weight he put upon them. His fingers did not pain him. He felt no sensations in them at all and his feet might have been pieces of wood strapped within his ski boots.

He crossed the river and angled up the slope towards the ridge that lay between him and the Moose. When he came out of the timber, the moon threw his shadow on the snow, a shadow faltering and stooped as if at any minute it might leave him, send him on alone to go shadowless through the moonlight. His shadow became a burden, something he pulled beside him in the snow.

He climbed high above the timber. The wind blew before him the long ends of the red neckerchief that he wore tied around the collar of his mackinaw, and near him the moon threw the outlines of a peak black upon the snow, black as ink seeping through the snow. Conroy paused a moment, leaned against a snow bank, sank down into it and rested.

How good to rest! How soft and warm the snow! There was the valley below him, empty in the moonlight—the clearing in the forest, timber that looked small and black as marsh grass. Across from him was a line of peaks thrust up against the sky, notched and jagged as if old bones, half-covered with the snow, littered their crests. To his left was the pass, a low saddle in the mountains, where he had crossed in the afternoon.

From below, somewhere in the forest, a wolf howled.

Conroy glanced upwards over his shoulder. He had still six hundred feet to climb to the ridge above the Moose, above the cabin at Terrace creek where MacMoran waited. MacMoran would take him in, feed him, make a fire for him to sit beside. He gathered his muscles together, summoned his strength that was slipping from him like a loosened garment. Then he lay back for another moment, to rest.

When he opened his eyes again, the moon had gone. The red sun, topping the range across the valley, shone upon him. His neckerchief flapped in the wind on the snow beside his cheek. He had slipped lower, fallen over upon his side, his face turned towards the route he had followed where his half-obliterated ski trail led down to the timber, the stunted spruce and balsam that seemed to be on their way towards him.

He heard horse bells. It was winter and no horses were within a hundred miles. He heard streaming river water. He heard a wide brown river running over mossy boulders between low banks of grass and willow. Across the valley he saw a cottage he had never seen before—a white cottage, low-roofed, with green trees beside it and an open door.

Then he remembered that he was on his way to MacMoran's cabin on Terrace Creek. MacMoran would be waiting for him. He tried to rise, but his arms stayed still at his side. Snow had drifted over them. A weight was on them that he could not lift. They were heavy with the burden of their own inertia. Snow like a blanket covered his body and the wind blew snow against his face.

For a moment he thought again of Macdonald who had brought his frozen feet to the railroad. Macdonald frowned and shook his head, opened his mouth and spoke some words that Conroy could not hear.

They would come and get him, Conroy thought—Macdonald, MacMoran, someone would come and get him. They were camped now down by Hoodoo cabin. They would see his trail and come and get him. He would lie for a while and wait.

Later, the pale cold sun was high in the sky. It shone full upon him. But the light of the sun was dim, as if a brighter light shone from behind it and the sunlight was its shadow. He could not see across the valley now, where the white cottage with the open door and the green trees had been. The world was growing small, dying slowly in the darkness of the sunlight.

Responding

1. What was Dave Conroy doing out in the wilderness?

2. At what point does the reader know the protagonist is in serious trouble and not likely to reach MacMoran's cabin?

3. What three critical mistakes did Conroy make? What are some things he could have done to prevent himself from freezing?

4. What effect does the setting of the story have on the plot and theme?

5. How is this story similar to others you have read or heard about people in the wilderness? How is it different?

6. Using details from the story, sketch a scene which might be used to illustrate this selection in a magazine such as *Reader's Digest*.

Student notes, page 245

Ray Bradbury

THE VELDT

Time: the future. Peter and Wendy have been reading too much about Africa. Now there's an African grassland in their nursery and their parents are getting a little concerned . . .

"George, I wish you'd look at the nursery."

"What's wrong with it?"

"I don't know."

"Well, then."

"I just want you to look at it, is all, or call a psychologist in to look at it."

"What would a psychologist want with a nursery?"

"You know very well what he'd want." His wife paused in the middle of the kitchen and watched the stove busy humming to itself, making supper for four.

"It's just that the nursery is different now than it was."

"All right, let's have a look."

They walked down the hall of their soundproofed Happylife Home, which had cost them thirty thousand dollars installed, this house which clothed and fed and rocked them to sleep and played and sang and was good to them. Their approach sensitized a switch somewhere and the nursery light flicked on when they came within ten feet of it. Similarly, behind them, in the halls, lights went on and off as they left them behind, with a soft automaticity.

"Well," said George Hadley.

They stood on the thatched floor of the nursery. It was forty feet across by forty feet long and thirty feet high; it had cost half again as much as the rest of the house. "But nothing's too good for our children," George had said.

The nursery was silent. It was empty as a jungle glade at hot high noon. The walls were blank and two-dimensional. Now, as George and Lydia Hadley stood in the center of the room, the walls began to purr and recede into crystalline distance, it seemed, and presently an African veldt appeared, in three dimensions; on all sides, in color reproduced to the final pebble and bit of straw. The ceiling above them became a deep sky with a hot yellow sun.

George Hadley felt the perspiration start on his brow.

"Let's get out of the sun," he said. "This is a little too real. But I don't see anything wrong."

"Wait a moment, you'll see," said his wife.

Now the hidden odorophonics were beginning to blow a wind of odor at the two people in the middle of the baked veldtland. The hot straw smell of lion grass, the cool green smell of the hidden water hole, the great rusty smell of animals, the smell of dust like a red paprika in the hot air. And now the sounds: the thump of distant antelope feet on grassy sod, the papery rustling of vultures. A shadow passed through the sky. The shadow flickered on George Hadley's upturned, sweating face.

"Filthy creatures," he heard his wife say.

"The vultures."

"You see, there are the lions, far over, that way. Now they're on their way to the water hole. They've just been eating," said Lydia. "I don't know what."

"Some animal." George Hadley put his hand up to shield off the burning light from his squinted eyes. "A zebra or a baby giraffe, maybe."

"Are you sure?" His wife sounded peculiarly tense.

"No, it's a little late to be sure," he said, amused. "Nothing over there I can see but cleaned bone, and the vultures dropping for what's left."

"Did you hear that scream?" she asked.

"No."

"About a minute ago?"

"Sorry, no."

The lions were coming. And again George Hadley was filled with admiration for the mechanical genius who had conceived this room. A miracle of efficiency selling for an absurdly low price. Every home should have one. Oh, occasionally they frightened you with their clinical accuracy, they startled you, gave you a twinge, but most of the time what fun for everyone, not only your own son and daughter, but for yourself when you felt like a quick jaunt to a foreign land, a quick change of scenery. Well, here it was!

And here were the lions now, fifteen feet away, so real, so feverishly and startlingly real that you could feel the prickling fur on your hand, and your mouth was stuffed with the dusty upholstery smell of their heated pelts, and the yellow of them was in your eyes like the yellow of an exquisite French tapestry, the yellows of lions and summer grass, and the sound of the matted lion lungs exhaling on the silent noontide, and the smell of meat from the panting, dripping mouths.

The lions stood looking at George and Lydia Hadley with terrible green-yellow eyes.

"Watch out!" screamed Lydia.

The lions came running at them.

Lydia bolted and ran. Instinctively, George sprang after her. Outside, in the hall, with the door slammed, he was laughing and she was crying, and they both stood appalled at the other's reaction.

"George!"

"Lydia! Oh, my dear poor sweet Lydia!"

"They almost got us!"

"Walls, Lydia, remember; crystal walls, that's all they are. Oh, they look real, I must admit—Africa in your parlor—but it's all dimensional, superreactionary, supersensitive color film and mental tape film behind glass screens. It's all odorophonics and sonics, Lydia. Here's my handkerchief."

"I'm afraid." She came to him and put her body against him and cried steadily. "Did you see? Did you *feel*? It's too real."

"Now, Lydia . . ."

"You've got to tell Wendy and Peter not to read any more on Africa."

"Of course—of course." He patted her.

"Promise?"

"Sure."

"And lock the nursery for a few days until I get my nerves settled."

"You know how difficult Peter is about that. When I punished him a month ago by locking the nursery for even a few hours—the tantrum he threw! And Wendy too. They *live* for the nursery."

"It's got to be locked, that's all there is to it."

"All right." Reluctantly he locked the huge door. "You've been working too hard. You need a rest."

"I don't know—I don't know," she said, blowing her nose, sitting down in a chair that immediately began to rock and comfort her. "Maybe I don't have enough to do. Maybe I have time to think too much. Why don't we shut the whole house off for a few days and take a vacation?"

"You mean you want to fry my eggs for me?"

"Yes." She nodded.

"And darn my socks?"

"Yes." A frantic, watery-eyed nodding.

"And sweep the house?"

"Yes, yes—oh, yes!"

"But I thought that's why we bought this house, so we wouldn't have to do anything?"

"That's just it. I feel like I don't belong here. The house is wife and mother now and nursemaid. Can I compete with an African veldt? Can I give a bath and scrub the children as efficiently or quickly as the automatic scrub bath can? I can not. And it isn't just me. It's you. You've been awfully nervous lately."

"I suppose I have been smoking too much."

"You look as if you didn't know what to do with yourself in this house, either. You smoke a little more every morning and drink a little more every afternoon and need a little more sedative every night. You're beginning to feel unnecessary too."

"Am I?" He paused and tried to feel into himself to see what was really there.

"Oh, George!" She looked beyond him, at the nursery door. "Those lions can't get out of there, can they?"

He looked at the door and saw it tremble as if something had jumped against it from the other side.

"Of course not," he said.

At dinner they ate alone, for Wendy and Peter were at a special plastic carnival across town and had televised home to say they'd be late, to go ahead eating. So George Hadley, bemused, sat watching the dining-room table produce warm dishes of food from its mechanical interior.

"We forgot the ketchup," he said.

"Sorry," said a small voice within the table, and ketchup appeared.

As for the nursery, thought George Hadley, it won't hurt for the children to be locked out of it awhile. Too much of anything isn't good for anyone. And it was clearly indicated that the children had been spending a little too much time on Africa. That sun. He could feel it on his neck, still, like a hot paw. And the lions. And the smell of blood. Remarkable how the nursery caught the telepathic emanations of the children's minds and created life to fill their every desire. The children thought lions, and there were lions. The children thought zebras, and there were zebras. Sun—sun. Giraffes—giraffes. Death and death.

That last. He chewed tastelessly on the meat that the table had cut for him. Death thoughts. They were awfully young, Wendy and Peter, for death thoughts. Or, no, you were never too young, really. Long before you knew what death was you were wishing it on someone else. When you were two years old, you were shooting people with cap pistols.

But this—the long, hot African veldt—the awful death in the jaws of a lion. And repeated again and again.

"Where are you going?"

He didn't answer Lydia. Preoccupied, he let the lights glow softly on ahead of him, extinguished behind him as he padded to the nursery door. He listened against it. Faraway, a lion roared.

He unlocked the door and opened it. Just before he stepped inside, he heard a faraway scream. And then another roar from the lions, which subsided quickly.

He stepped into Africa. How many times in the last year had he opened this door and found Wonderland, Alice, the Mock Turtle, or Aladdin and his Magical Lamp, or Jack Pumpkinhead of Oz, or Dr. Doolittle, or the cow jumping over a very real-appearing moon —all the delightful contraptions of a make-believe world. How often had he seen Pegasus flying in the sky ceiling, or seen fountains of red fireworks, or heard angel voices singing. But now, this yellow hot Africa, this bake oven with murder in the heat. Perhaps Lydia was right. Perhaps they needed a little vacation from the fantasy which was growing a bit too real for ten-year-old children. It was all right to exercise one's mind with gymnastic fantasies, but when the lively child mind settled on *one* pattern ... ? It seemed that, at a distance, for the past month, he had heard lions roaring, and smelled their strong odor seeping as far away as his study door. But, being busy, he had paid it no attention.

George Hadley stood on the African grassland alone. The lions looked up from their feeding, watching him. The only flaw to the illusion was the open door through which he could see his wife, far down the dark hall, like a framed picture, eating her dinner abstractedly.

"Go away," he said to the lions.

They did not go.

He knew the principle of the room exactly. You sent out your thoughts. Whatever you thought would appear.

"Let's have Aladdin and his lamp," he snapped.

The veldtland remained; the lions remained.

"Come on, room! I demand Aladdin!" he said.

Nothing happened. The lions mumbled in their baked pelts.

"Aladdin!"

He went back to dinner. "The fool room's out of order," he said. "It won't respond."

"Or——"

"Or what?"

"Or it *can't* respond," said Lydia, "because the children have thought about Africa and lions and killing so many days that the room's in a rut."

"Could be."

"Or Peter's set it to remain that way."

"*Set* it?"

"He may have got into the machinery and fixed something."

"Peter doesn't know machinery."

"He's a wise one for ten. That I.Q. of his——"

"Nevertheless——"

"Hello, Mom. Hello, Dad."

The Hadleys turned. Wendy and Peter were coming in the front door, cheeks like peppermint candy, eyes like bright blue agate marbles, a smell of ozone on their jumpers from their trip in the helicopter.

"You're just in time for supper," said both parents.

"We're full of strawberry ice cream and hot dogs," said the children, holding hands. "But we'll sit and watch."

"Yes, come tell us about the nursery," said George Hadley.

The brother and sister blinked at him and then at each other. "Nursery?"

"All about Africa and everything," said the father with false joviality.

"I don't understand," said Peter.

"Your mother and I were just traveling through Africa with rod and reel; Tom Swift and his Electric Lion," said George Hadley.

"There's no Africa in the nursery," said Peter simply.

"Oh, come now, Peter. We know better."

"I don't remember any Africa," said Peter to Wendy. "Do you?"

"No."

"Run see and come tell."

She obeyed.

"Wendy, come back here!" said George Hadley, but she was gone. The house lights followed her like a flock of fireflies. Too late, he realized he had forgotten to lock the nursery door after his last inspection.

"Wendy'll look and come tell us," said Peter.

"She doesn't have to tell *me*. I've seen it."

"I'm sure you're mistaken, Father."

"I'm not, Peter. Come along now."

But Wendy was back. "It's not Africa," she said breathlessly.

"We'll see about this," said George Hadley, and they all walked down the hall together and opened the nursery door.

There was a green, lovely forest, a lovely river, a purple mountain, high voices singing, and Rima, lovely and mysterious, lurking in the trees with colorful flights of butterflies, like animated bouquets, lingering on her long hair. The African veldtland was gone. The lions were gone. Only Rima was here now, singing a song so beautiful that it brought tears to your eyes.

George Hadley looked in at the changed scene. "Go to bed," he said to the children.

They opened their mouths.

"You heard me," he said.

They went off to the air closet, where a wind sucked them like brown leaves up the flue to their slumber rooms.

George Hadley walked through the singing glade and picked up something that lay in the corner near where the lions had been. He walked slowly back to his wife.

"What is that?" she asked.

"An old wallet of mine," he said.

He showed it to her. The smell of hot grass was on it and the smell of a lion. There were drops of saliva on it, it had been chewed, and there were blood smears on both sides.

He closed the nursery door and locked it, tight.

In the middle of the night he was still awake and he knew his wife was awake. "Do you think Wendy changed it?" she said at last, in the dark room.

"Of course."

"Made it from a veldt into a forest and put Rima there instead of lions?"

"Yes."

"Why?"

"I don't know. But it's staying locked until I find out."

"How did your wallet get there?"

"I don't know anything," he said, "except that I'm beginning to be sorry we bought that room for the children. If children are neurotic at all, a room like that——"

"It's supposed to help them work off their neuroses in a healthful way."

"I'm starting to wonder." He stared at the ceiling.

"We've given the children everything they ever wanted. Is this our reward—secrecy, disobedience?"

"Who was it said, 'Children are carpets, they should be stepped on occasionally'? We've never lifted a hand. They're insufferable— let's admit it. They come and go when they like; they treat us as if *we* were offspring. They're spoiled and we're spoiled."

"They've been acting funny ever since you forbade them to take the rocket to New York a few months ago."

"They're not old enough to do that alone, I explained."

"Nevertheless, I've noticed they've been decidedly cool toward us since."

"I think I'll have David McClean come tomorrow morning to have a look at Africa."

"But it's not Africa now, it's Green Mansions country and Rima."

"I have a feeling it'll be Africa again before then."

A moment later they heard the screams.

Two screams. Two people screaming from downstairs. And then a roar of lions.

"Wendy and Peter aren't in their rooms," said his wife.

He lay in his bed with his beating heart. "No," he said. "They've broken into the nursery."

"Those screams—they sound familiar."

"Do they?"

"Yes, awfully."

And although their beds tried very hard, the two adults couldn't be rocked to sleep for another hour. A smell of cats was in the night air.

"Father?" said Peter.

"Yes."

Peter looked at his shoes. He never looked at his father any more, nor at his mother. "You aren't going to lock up the nursery for good, are you?"

"That all depends."

"On what?" snapped Peter.

"On you and your sister. If you intersperse this Africa with a little variety—oh, Sweden perhaps, or Denmark or China——"

"I thought we were free to play as we wished."

"You are, within reasonable bounds."

"What's wrong with Africa, Father?"

"Oh, so now you admit you have been conjuring up Africa, do you?"

"I wouldn't want the nursery locked up," said Peter coldly. "Ever."

"Matter of fact, we're thinking of turning the whole house off for about a month. Live sort of a carefree one-for-all existence."

"That sounds dreadful! Would I have to tie my own shoes instead of letting the shoe tier do it? And brush my own teeth and comb my hair and give myself a bath?"

"It would be fun for a change, don't you think?"

"No, it would be horrid. I didn't like it when you took out the picture painter last month."

"That's because I wanted you to learn to paint all by yourself, son."

"I don't want to do anything but look and listen and smell; what else *is* there to do?"

"All right, go play in Africa."

"Will you shut off the house sometime soon?"

"We're considering it."

"I don't think you'd better consider it any more, Father."

"I won't have any threats from my son!"

"Very well." And Peter strolled off to the nursery.

"Am I on time?" said David McClean.

"Breakfast?" asked George Hadley.

"Thanks, had some. What's the trouble?"

"David, you're a psychologist."

"I should hope so."

"Well, then, have a look at our nursery. You saw it a year ago when you dropped by; did you notice anything peculiar about it then?"

"Can't say I did; the usual violences, a tendency toward a slight paranoia here or there, usual in children because they feel persecuted by parents constantly, but, oh, really nothing."

They walked down the hall. "I locked the nursery up," explained the father, "and the children broke back into it during the night. I let them stay so they could form the patterns for you to see."

There was a terrible screaming from the nursery.

"There it is," said George Hadley. "See what you make of it."

They walked in on the children without rapping.

The screams had faded. The lions were feeding.

"Run outside a moment, children," said George Hadley. "No, don't change the mental combination. Leave the walls as they are. Get!"

With the children gone, the two men stood studying the lions clustered at a distance, eating with great relish whatever it was they had caught.

"I wish I knew what it was," said George Hadley. "Sometimes I can almost see. Do you think if I brought high-powered binoculars here and——"

David McClean laughed dryly. "Hardly." He turned to study all four walls. "How long has this been going on?"

"A little over a month."

"It certainly doesn't *feel* good."

"I want facts, not feelings."

"My dear George, a psychologist never saw a fact in his life. He only hears about feelings; vague things. This doesn't feel good, I tell you. Trust my hunches and my instincts. I have a nose for something bad. This is very bad. My advice to you is to have the whole damn room torn down and your children brought to me every day during the next year for treatment."

"Is it that bad?"

"I'm afraid so. One of the original uses of these nurseries was so that we could study the patterns left on the walls by the child's mind, study at our leisure, and help the child. In this case, however, the room has become a channel toward—destructive thoughts, instead of a release away from them."

"Didn't you sense this before?"

"I sensed only that you had spoiled your children more than most. And now you're letting them down in some way. What way?"

"I wouldn't let them go to New York."

"What else?"

"I've taken a few machines from the house and threatened them, a month ago, with closing up the nursery unless they did their homework. I did close it for a few days to show I meant business."

"Ah, ha!"

"Does that mean anything?"

"Everything. Where before they had a Santa Claus now they have a Scrooge. Children prefer Santas. You've let this room and this house replace you and your wife in your children's affections. This room is their mother and father, far more important in their lives than their real parents. And now you come along and want to shut it off. No wonder there's hatred here. You can feel it coming out of the sky. Feel that sun. George, you'll have to change your life. Like too many others, you've built it around creature comforts. Why, you'd starve tomorrow if something went wrong in your kitchen. You wouldn't know how to tap an egg. Nevertheless, turn everything off. Start new. It'll take time. But we'll make good children out of bad in a year, wait and see."

"But won't the shock be too much for the children, shutting the room up abruptly, for good?"

"I don't want them going any deeper into this, that's all."

The lions were finished with their red feast.

The lions were standing on the edge of the clearing watching the two men.

"Now *I'm* feeling persecuted," said McClean. "Let's get out of here. I never have cared for these damned rooms. Make me nervous."

"The lions look real, don't they?" said George Hadley. "I don't suppose there's any way——"

"What?"

"——that they could *become* real?"

"Not that I know."

"Some flaw in the machinery, a tampering or something?"

"No."

They went to the door.

"I don't imagine the room will like being turned off," said the father.

"Nothing ever likes to die—even a room."

"I wonder if it hates me for wanting to switch it off?"

"Paranoia is thick around here today," said David McClean. "You can follow it like a spoor. Hello." He bent and picked up a bloody scarf. "This yours?"

"No." George Hadley's face was rigid. "It belongs to Lydia."

They went to the fuse box together and threw the switch that killed the nursery.

The two children were in hysterics. They screamed and pranced and threw things. They yelled and sobbed and swore and jumped at the furniture.

"You can't do that to the nursery, you can't!"

"Now, children."

The children flung themselves onto a couch, weeping.

"George," said Lydia Hadley, "turn on the nursery, just for a few moments. You can't be so abrupt."

"No."

"You can't be so cruel."

"Lydia, it's off, and it stays off. And the whole damn house dies as of here and now. The more I see of the mess we've put ourselves in, the more it sickens me. We've been contemplating our mechanical, electronic navels for too long. My God, how we need a breath of honest air!"

And he marched about the house turning off the voice clocks, the stoves, the heaters, the shoe shiners, the shoe lacers, the body scrubbers and swabbers and massagers, and every other machine he could put his hand to.

The house was full of dead bodies, it seemed. It felt like a mechanical cemetery. So silent. None of the humming hidden energy of machines waiting to function at the tap of a button.

"Don't let them do it!" wailed Peter at the ceiling, as if he was talking to the house, the nursery. "Don't let Father kill everything." He turned to his father. "Oh, I hate you!"

"Insults won't get you anywhere."

"I wish you were dead!"

"We were, for a long while. Now we're going to really start living. Instead of being handled and massaged, we're going to *live*."

Wendy was still crying and Peter joined her again. "Just a moment, just one moment, just another moment of nursery," they wailed.

"Oh, George," said the wife, "it can't hurt."

"All right—all right, if they'll only just shut up. One minute, mind you, and then off forever."

"Daddy, Daddy, Daddy!" sang the children, smiling with wet faces.

"And then we're going on a vacation. David McClean is coming back in half an hour to help us move out and get to the airport. I'm going to dress. You turn the nursery on for a minute, Lydia, just a minute, mind you."

And the three of them went babbling off while he let himself be vacuumed upstairs through the air flue and set about dressing himself. A minute later Lydia appeared.

"I'll be glad when we get away," she sighed.

"Did you leave them in the nursery?"

"I wanted to dress too. Oh, that horrid Africa. What can they see in it?"

"Well, in five minutes we'll be on our way to Iowa. Lord, how did we ever get in this house? What prompted us to buy a nightmare?"

"Pride, money, foolishness."

"I think we'd better get downstairs before those kids get engrossed with those damned beasts again."

Just then they heard the children calling, "Daddy, Mommy, come quick—quick!"

They went downstairs in the air flue and ran down the hall. The children were nowhere in sight. "Wendy? Peter!"

They ran into the nursery. The veldtland was empty save for the lions waiting, looking at them. "Peter, Wendy?"

The door slammed.

"Wendy, Peter!"

George Hadley and his wife whirled and ran back to the door.

"Open the door!" cried George Hadley, trying the knob. "Why, they've locked it from the outside! Peter!" He beat at the door. "Open up!"

He heard Peter's voice outside, against the door.

"Don't let them switch off the nursery and the house," he was saying.

Mr. and Mrs. George Hadley beat at the door. "Now, don't be ridiculous, children. It's time to go. Mr. McClean'll be here in a minute and . . ."

And then they heard the sounds.

The lions on three sides of them, in the yellow veldt grass, padding through the dry straw, rumbling and roaring in their throats.

The lions.

Mr. Hadley looked at his wife and they turned and looked back at the beasts edging slowly forward, crouching, tails stiff.

Mr. and Mrs. Hadley screamed.

And suddenly they realized why those other screams had sounded familiar.

"Well, here I am," said David McClean in the nursery doorway. "Oh, hello." He stared at the two children seated in the center of the open glade eating a little picnic lunch. Beyond them was the water hole and the yellow veldtland; above was the hot sun. He began to perspire. "Where are your father and mother?"

The children looked up and smiled. "Oh, they'll be here directly."

"Good, we must get going." At a distance Mr. McClean saw the lions fighting and clawing and then quieting down to feed in silence under the shady trees.

He squinted at the lions with his hand up to his eyes.

Now the lions were done feeding. They moved to the water hole to drink.

A shadow flickered over Mr. McClean's hot face. Many shadows flickered. The vultures were dropping down the blazing sky.

"A cup of tea?" asked Wendy in the silence.

Responding

1. What unusual technology in the story suggests a futuristic setting? How does the nursery work? Is it functioning properly in the story?

2. What mental and emotional effects does the veldt have on a) the children b) the parents and c) the psychologist?

3. What explanation can you give for the father's wallet and the mother's scarf being in the nursery? What does this suggest about the events to follow?

4. How does the author create and maintain suspense?

5. Find allusions to mythology and children's literature and explain their roles in the story.

6. What comments does Bradbury's story make about a) the generation gap b) the nature of children and c) the influence of technology on people today? What is your response to each of these comments?

Student notes, page 246

Roald Dahl

THE WISH

Transformed by the fancy of an imaginative boy, an ordinary carpet becomes a gameboard for adventure—and terror!

*U*under the palm of one hand the child became aware of the scab of an old cut on his kneecap. He bent forward to examine it closely. A scab was always a fascinating thing; it presented a special challenge he was never able to resist.

Yes, he thought, I will pick it off, even if it isn't ready, even if the middle of it sticks, even if it hurts like anything.

With a fingernail he began to explore cautiously around the edges of the scab. He got the nail underneath it, and when he raised it, but ever so slightly, it suddenly came off, the whole hard brown scab came off beautifully, leaving an interesting little circle of smooth red skin.

Nice. Very nice indeed. He rubbed the circle and it didn't hurt. He picked up the scab, put it on his thigh and flipped it with a finger so that it flew away and landed on the edge of the carpet, the enormous red and black and yellow carpet that stretched the whole length of the hall from the stairs on which he sat to the front door in the distance. A tremendous carpet. Bigger than the tennis lawn. Much bigger than that. He regarded it gravely, settling his eyes upon it with mild pleasure. He had never really noticed it before, but now, all of a sudden, the colors seemed to brighten mysteriously and spring out at him in a most dazzling way.

You see, he told himself, I know how it is. The red parts of the carpet are red-hot lumps of coal. What I must do is this: I must walk all the way along it to the front door without touching them. If I touch the red I will be burnt. As a matter of fact, I will be burnt up completely. And the black parts of the carpet . . . yes, the black parts are snakes, poisonous snakes, adders mostly, and cobras, thick like tree-trunks round the middle, and if I touch one of *them*, I'll be bitten and I'll die before tea-time. And if I get across safely, without being burnt and without being bitten, I will be given a puppy for my birthday tomorrow.

He got to his feet and climbed higher up the stairs to obtain a better view of this vast tapestry of colour and death. Was it possible? Was there enough yellow? Yellow was the only color he was allowed to walk on. Could it be done? This was not a journey to be undertaken lightly; the risks were too great for that. The child's face —a fringe of white-gold hair, two large blue eyes, a small pointed chin—peered down anxiously over the banisters. The yellow was a bit thin in places and there were one or two widish gaps, but it did seem to go all the way along to the other end. For someone who had only yesterday triumphantly travelled the whole length of the brick path from the stables to the summerhouse without touching the cracks, this carpet thing should not be too difficult. Except for the snakes. The mere thought of snakes sent a fine electricity of fear running like pins down the backs of his legs and under the soles of his feet.

He came slowly down the stairs and advanced to the edge of the carpet. He extended one small sandalled foot and placed it cautiously upon a patch of yellow. Then he brought the other foot up, and there was just enough room for him to stand with the two feet together. There! He had started! His bright oval face was curiously intent, a shade whiter perhaps than before, and he was holding his arms out sideways to assist his balance. He took another step, lifting his foot high over a patch of black, aiming carefully with his toe for a narrow channel of yellow on the other side. When he had completed the second step he paused to rest, standing very stiff and still. The narrow channel of yellow ran forward unbroken for at least five yards and he advanced gingerly along it, bit by bit, as though walking a tightrope. Where it finally curled off sideways, he had to take another long stride, this time over a vicious-looking mixture of black and red. Halfway across he began to wobble. He waved his arms around wildly, windmill fashion, to keep his balance and he got across safely and rested again on the other side. He was quite breathless now, and so tense he stood high on his toes all the time, arms out sideways, fists clenched. He was on a big safe island of yellow. There was lots of room on it, he couldn't possibly fall off, and he stood there resting, hesitating, waiting, wishing he could stay for ever on this big safe yellow island. But the fear of not getting the puppy compelled him to go on.

Step by step, he edged further ahead, and between each one he paused to decide exactly where next he should put his foot. Once, he had a choice of ways, either to left or right, and he chose the left because although it seemed the more difficult, there was not so much black in that direction. The black was what made him nervous. He glanced quickly over his shoulder to see how far he had come. Nearly halfway. There could be no turning back now. He was in the middle and he couldn't turn back and he couldn't jump off sideways either because it was too far, and when he looked at all the red and all the black that lay ahead of him, he felt that old sudden sickening surge of panic in his chest—like last Easter time, that afternoon when he got lost all alone in the darkest part of Piper's Wood.

He took another step, placing his foot carefully upon the only little piece of yellow within reach, and this time the point of the foot came within a centimetre of some black. It wasn't touching the black, he could see it wasn't touching, he could see the small line of yellow separating the toe of his sandal from the black; but the snake stirred as though sensing the nearness, and raised its head and gazed at the foot with bright beady eyes, watching to see if it was going to touch.

"I'm not touching you! You mustn't bite me! You know I'm not touching you!"

Another snake slid up noiselessly beside the first, raised its head, two heads now, two pairs of eyes staring at the foot, gazing at a little naked place just below the sandal strap where the skin showed through. The child went high up on his toes and stayed there, frozen stiff with terror. It was minutes before he dared to move again.

The next step would have to be a really long one. There was this deep curling river of black that ran clear across the width of the carpet, and he was forced by this position to cross it at its widest part. He thought first of trying to jump it, but decided he couldn't be sure of landing accurately on the narrow band of yellow the other side. He took a deep breath, lifted one foot, and inch by inch he pushed it out in front of him, far far out, then down and down until at last the tip of his sandal was across and resting safely on the edge of the yellow. He leaned forward, transferring his weight to his front foot. Then he tried to bring the back foot up as well. He strained and pulled and jerked his body, but the legs were too wide apart and he couldn't make it. He tried to get back again. He couldn't do that either. He was doing the splits and he was properly stuck. He glanced down and saw this deep curling river of black underneath him. Parts of it were stirring now, and uncoiling and sliding and beginning to shine with a dreadfully oily glister. He wobbled, waved his arms frantically to keep his balance, but that seemed to make it worse. He was starting to go over. He was going over to the right, quite slowly he was going over, then faster and faster, and at the last moment, instinctively he put out a hand to break the fall and the next thing he saw was this bare hand of his going right into the middle of a great glistening mass of black and he gave one piercing cry of terror as it touched.

Outside in the sunshine, far away behind the house, the mother was looking for her son.

Responding

1. The author is successful in presenting the perspective of an imaginative preschooler in this story. Give three examples of words or sentences and explain how they convey a sense of the protagonist's preschool age to you.

2. Why does the author change points of view at the end of the story? Does this shift in point of view add to or detract from the impact and realism of the story? Comment.

3. Why is this story called "The Wish"? Suggest an alternate title and provide reasons for your choice.

4. Using adjectives, describe the atmosphere of this story.

5. Tell about a childhood game similar to the boy's which you once played by yourself, *or* describe a childhood fear you used to have.

6. Using images from the story, write a short free verse poem (no regular rhyme, rhythm, or line structure) about the boy's experience.

Student notes, page 246

5 POINT OF VIEW

Many times in a typical week we may share a story about what happened during our day, or we may retell an entertaining story related to us by a friend or family member. Whether we are telling a story about ourselves or about someone else, we are limited in what we know and can relate. In a story about ourselves, we can tell our own thoughts and feelings with considerable depth, but we may not know with certainty those of anyone else. In the same way, we may tell a story about other people and know reasonably well the thoughts and feelings of everyone involved because we have talked to each of them and heard their feelings. Then, we would relate only those details that make an interesting, meaningful story.

The teller of the tale, or the narrator, whether in life or literature, sees the story through his or her own eyes and interprets the events for us. This special point of view gives a story its unity and helps the reader see the events and details from a particular perspective. Told through the eyes of an observant narrator, a story will come alive and draw the reader into its world.

The selections in this chapter offer readers experiences with three different points of view. The first story, "Images," is told through the eyes of a little girl who is a participant in the events, and who shares her feelings of loneliness along with her insights. The second story, told through the eyes of someone outside the story reveals the thoughts and feelings of Carolee Mitchell as she becomes involved in "A Television Drama." "The Sentimentalists," lets us see a series of events through the eyes of one observer, whose faith in himself and human nature is shaken by what takes place.

To appreciate how a story works, then, we must ask who is telling the tale. Whether we are listening to a friend or reading a story in a book, our impressions of the events and of the characters are shaped by what the storyteller allows us to know. This simple but significant observation is what makes point of view important to consider.

Alice Munro

IMGES

A young farm girl goes muskrat-trapping with her father—and find another
world she never knew of. . . .

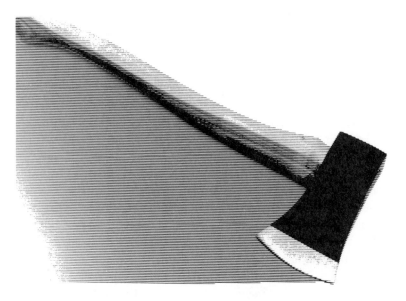

Now that Mary McQuade had come, I pretended not to remember her. It seemed the wisest thing to do. She herself said, "If you don't remember me you don't remember much," but let the matter drop, just once adding, "I bet you never went to your Grandma's house last summer. I bet you don't remember that either."

It was called, even that summer, my grandma's house, though my grandfather was then still alive. He had withdrawn into one room, the largest front bedroom. It had wooden shutters on the inside of the windows, like the living room and dining room; the other bedrooms had only blinds. Also, the veranda kept out the light so that my grandfather lay in near-darkness all day, with his white hair, now washed and tended and soft as a baby's, and his white nightshirt and pillows, making an island in the room which people approached with diffidence, but resolutely. Mary McQuade in her uniform was the other island in the room, and she sat mostly not moving where the fan, as if it was tired, stirred the air like soup. It must have been too dark to read or knit, supposing she wanted to do those things, and so she merely waited and breathed, making a sound like the fan made, full of old indefinable complaint.

I was so young then I was put to sleep in a crib—not at home but this was what was kept for me at my grandma's house—in a room across the hall. There was no fan there and the dazzle of outdoors— all the flat fields round the house turned, in the sun, to the brilliance of water—made lightning cracks in the drawn-down blinds. Who could sleep? My mother's my grandmother's my aunts' voices wove their ordinary repetitions, on the veranda in the kitchen in the dining room (where with a little brass-handled brush my mother cleaned the white cloth, and the lighting-fixture over the round table hung down unlit flowers of thick, butterscotch glass). All the meals in that house, the cooking, the visiting, the conversation, even someone playing on the piano (it was my youngest aunt, Edith, not married, singing and playing with one hand, *Nita, Juanita, softly falls the southern moon*); all this life going on. Yet the ceilings of the rooms were very high and under them was a great deal of dim wasted space, and when I lay in my crib too hot to sleep I could look up and see that emptiness, the stained corners, and feel, without knowing what it was, just what everybody else in the house must have felt—under the sweating heat the fact of death-contained, that little lump of magic ice. And Mary McQuade waiting in her starched white dress, big and gloomy as an iceberg herself, implacable, waiting and breathing. I held her responsible.

So I pretended not to remember her. She had not put on her white uniform, which did not really make her less dangerous but might mean, at least, that the time of her power had not yet come. Out in the daylight, and not dressed in white, she turned out to be freckled all over, everywhere you could see, as if she was sprinkled with oatmeal, and she had a crown of frizzy, glinting, naturally brass-colored hair. Her voice was loud and hoarse and complaint was her everyday language. "Am I going to have to hang up this

wash all by myself?" she shouted at me, in the yard, and I followed
her to the clothesline platform where with a groan she let down the
basket of wet clothes. "Hand me them clothespins. One at a time.
Hand me them right side up. I shouldn't be out in this wind at all,
I've got a bronchial condition." Head hung, like an animal chained
to her side, I fed her clothespins. Outdoors, in the cold March air,
she lost some of her bulk and her smell. In the house I could always
smell her, even in the rooms she seldom entered. What was her
smell like? It was like metal and like some dark spice (cloves—she
did suffer from toothache) and like the preparation rubbed on my
chest when I had a cold. I mentioned it once to my mother, who
said, "Don't be silly, *I* don't smell anything." so I never told about
the taste, and there was a taste too. It was in all the food Mary
McQuade prepared and perhaps in all food eaten in her presence—
in my porridge at breakfast and my fried potatoes at noon and the
slice of bread and butter and brown sugar she gave me to eat in the
yard—something foreign, gritty, depressing. How could my parents
not know about it? But for reasons of their own they would pretend.
This was something I had not known a year ago.

After she had hung out the wash she had to soak her feet. Her
legs came straight up, round as drainpipes, from the steaming
basin. One hand on each knee, she bent into the steam and gave
grunts of pain and satisfaction.

"Are you a nurse?" I said, greatly daring, though my mother had
said she was.

"Yes I am and I wish I wasn't."

"Are you my aunt too?"

"If I was your Aunt you would call me Aunt Mary, wouldn't
you? Well you don't, do you? I'm your cousin, I'm your father's
cousin. That's why they get me instead of getting an ordinary
nurse. I'm a practical nurse. And there is always somebody sick in
this family and I got to go to them. I never get a rest."

I doubted this. I doubted that she was asked to come. She came,
and cooked what she liked and rearranged things to suit herself,
complaining about drafts, and let her power loose in the house. If
she had never come my mother would never have taken to her
bed.

My mother's bed was set up in the dining room, to spare Mary
McQuade climbing the stairs. My mother's hair was done in two

little thin dark braids, her cheeks were sallow, her neck warm and smelling of raisins as it always did, but the rest of her under the covers had changed into some large, fragile and mysterious object, difficult to move. She spoke of herself gloomily in the third person, saying, "Be careful, don't hurt Mother, don't sit on Mother's legs." Every time she said Mother I felt chilled, and a kind of wretchedness and shame spread through me as it did at the name of Jesus. This *Mother* that my own real, warm-necked, irascible and comforting human mother set up between us was an everlastingly wounded phantom, sorrowing like Him over all the wickedness I did not yet know I would commit.

My mother crocheted squares for an afghan, in all shades of purple. They fell among the bedclothes and she did not care. Once they were finished she forgot about them. She had forgotten all her stories which were about Princes in the Tower and a queen getting her head chopped off while a little dog was hiding under her dress and another queen sucking poison out of her husband's wound; and also about her own childhood, a time as legendary to me as any other. Given over to Mary's care she whimpered childishly, "Mary, I'm dying for you to rub my back." "Mary, could you make me a cup of tea? I feel if I drink any more tea I'm going to bob up to the ceiling, just like a big balloon, but you know it's all I want." Mary laughed shortly. "You," she said, "You're not going to bob up anywhere. Take a derrick to move *you*. Come on now, raise up, you'll be worse before you're better!" She shooed me off the bed and began to pull the sheets about with not very gentle jerks. "You been tiring your Momma out? What do you want to bother your Momma for on this nice a day?" "I think she's lonesome," my mother said, a weak and insincere defence. "She can be lonesome in the yard just as well as here," said Mary, with her grand, vague, menacing air. "You put your things on, out you go!"

My father, too, had altered since her coming. When he came in for his meals she was always waiting for him, some joke swelling her up like a bullfrog, making her ferocious-looking and red in the face. She put uncooked white beans in his soup, hard as pebbles, and waited to see if good manners would make him eat them. She stuck something to the bottom of his water glass to look like a fly. She gave him a fork with a prong missing, pretending it was by accident. He threw it at her, and missed, but startled me considerably.

My mother and father, eating supper, talked quietly and seriously. But in my father's family even grownups played tricks with rubber worms and beetles, fat aunts were always invited to sit on little rickety chairs and uncles broke wind in public and said, "Whoa, hold on there!" proud of themselves as if they had whistled a complicated tune. Nobody could ask your age without a rigmarole of teasing. So with Mary McQuade my father returned to family ways, just as he went back to eating heaps of fried potatoes and side meat and thick, floury pies, and drinking tea black and strong as medicine out of a tin pot, saying gratefully, "Mary, you know what it is a man ought to eat!" He followed that up with, "Don't you think it's time you got a man of your own to feed?" which earned him, not a fork thrown, but the dishrag.

His teasing of Mary was always about husbands. "I thought up one for you this morning!" he would say. "Now Mary I'm not fooling you, you give this some consideration." Her laughter would come out first in little angry puffs and explosions through her shut lips, while her face grew redder than you would have thought possible and her body twitched and rumbled threateningly in its chair. There was no doubt she enjoyed all this, all these preposterous imagined matings, though my mother would certainly have said it was cruel, cruel and indecent, to tease an old maid about men. In my father's family of course it was what she was always teased about, what else was there? And the heavier and coarser and more impossible she became, the more she would be teased. A bad thing in that family was to have them say you were *sensitive*, as they did of my mother. All the aunts and cousins and uncles had grown tremendously hardened to any sort of personal cruelty, reckless, even proud, it seemed, of a failure or deformity that could make for general laughter.

At supper-time it was dark in the house, in spite of the lengthening days. We did not yet have electricity. It came in soon afterwards, maybe the next summer. But at present there was a lamp on the table. In its light my father and Mary McQuade threw gigantic shadows, whose heads wagged clumsily with their talk and laughing. I watched the shadows instead of the people. They said, "What are you dreaming about?" but I was not dreaming, I was trying to understand the danger, to read the signs of invasion.

My father said, "Do you want to come with me and look at the traps?" He had a trapline for muskrats along the river. When he was younger he used to spend days, nights, weeks in the bush, following creeks all up and down Wawanash County, and he trapped not only muskrat then but red fox, wild mink, marten, all animals whose coats are prime in the fall. Muskrat is the only thing you can trap in the spring. Now that he was married and settled down to farming he just kept the one line, and that for only a few years. This may have been the last year he had it.

We went across a field that had been plowed the previous fall. There was a little snow lying in the furrows but it was not real snow, it was a thin crust like frosted glass that I could shatter with my heels. The field went downhill slowly, down to the river flats. The fence was down in some places from the weight of the snow; we could step over it.

My father's boots went ahead. His boots were to me as unique and familiar, as much an index to himself as his face was. When he had taken them off they stood in a corner of the kitchen, giving off a complicated smell of manure, machine oil, caked black mud, and the ripe and disintegrating material that lined their soles. They were a part of himself, temporarily discarded, waiting. They had an expression that was dogged and uncompromising, even brutal, and I thought of that as part of my father's look, the counterpart of his face, with its readiness for jokes and courtesies. Nor did that brutality surprise me; my father came back to us always, to my mother and me, from places where our judgment could not follow.

For instance, there was a muskrat in the trap. At first I saw it waving at the edge of the water, like something tropical, a dark fern. My father drew it up and the hairs ceased waving, clung together, the fern became a tail with the body of the rat attached to it, sleek and dripping. Its teeth were bared, its eyes wet on top, dead and dull beneath, glinted like washed pebbles. My father shook it and whirled it around, making a little rain of icy river water. "This is a good old rat," he said. "This is a big old king rat. Look at his tail!" Then perhaps thinking that I was worried, or perhaps only wanting to show me the charm of simple, perfect mechanical devices, he lifted the trap out of the water and explained to me how it worked, dragging the rat's head under at once and mercifully drowning him.

I did not understand or care. I only wanted, but did not dare, to touch the stiff, soaked body, a fact of death.

My father baited the trap again using some pieces of yellow, winter-wrinkled apple. He put the rat's body in a dark sack which he carried slung over his shoulder, like a pedlar in a picture. when he cut the apple I had seen the skinning knife, its slim bright blade.

Then we went along the river, the Wawanash River, which was high, running full, silver in the middle where the sun hit it and where it arrowed in to its swiftest motion. That is the current, I thought, and I pictured the current as something separate from the water, just as the wind was separate from the air and had its own invading shape. The banks were steep and slippery and lined with willow bushes, still bare and bent over and looking weak as grass. The noise the river made was not loud but deep, and seemed to come from away down in the middle of it, some hidden place where the water issued with a roar from underground.

The river curved, I lost my sense of direction. In the traps we found more rats, released them, shook them and hid them in the sack, replaced the bait. My face, my hands, my feet grew cold, but I did not mention it. I could not, to my father. And he never told me to be careful, to stay away from the edge of the water, he took it for granted that I would have sense enough not to fall in. I never asked how far we were going, or if the trapline would ever end. After a while there was a bush behind us, the afternoon darkened. It did not occur to me, not till long afterwards, that this was the same bush you could see from our yard, a fan-shaped hill rising up in the middle of it with bare trees in wintertime that looked like bony little twigs against the sky.

Now the bank, instead of willows, grew thick bushes higher than my head. I stayed on the path, about halfway up the bank, while my father went down to the water. When he bent over the trap, I could no longer see him. I looked around slowly and saw something else. Further along, and higher up the bank, a man was making his way down. He made no noise coming through the bushes and moved easily, as if he followed a path I could not see. At first I could just see his head and the upper part of his body. He was dark, with a high bald forehead, hair long behind the ears, deep vertical creases in his cheeks. When the bushes thinned I could see the rest of him, his long clever legs, thinness, drab camouflaging clothes, and what he carried in his hand, gleaming where the sun caught it—a little axe, or hatchet.

I never moved to warn or call my father. the man crossed my path somewhere ahead, continuing down to the river. People say they have been paralyzed by fear, but I was transfixed, as if struck by lightning, and what hit me did not feel like fear so much as recognition. I was not surprised. This is the sight that does not surprise you, the thing you have always known was there that comes so naturally, moving delicately and contentedly and in no hurry, as if it was made, in the first place, from a wish of yours, a hope of something final, terrifying. All my life I had known there was a man like this and he was behind doors, around the corner at the dark end of a hall. So now I saw him and just waited, like a child in an old negative, electrified against the dark noon sky, with glazing hair and burned-out Orphan Annie eyes. The man slipped down through the bushes to my father. And I never thought, or even hoped for, anything but the worst.

My father did not know. When he straightened up, the man was not three feet away from him and hid him from me. I heard my father's voice come out, after a moment's delay, quiet and neighborly.

"Hello, Joe. Well. Joe. I haven't seen you in a long time."

The man did not say a word, but edged around my father giving him a close look. "Joe, you know me," my father told him. "Ben Jordan. I been out looking at my traps. There's a lot of good rats in the river this year, Joe."

The man gave a quick not-trusting look at the trap my father had baited.

"You ought to set a line out yourself."

No answer. The man took his hatchet and chopped lightly at the air.

"Too late this year, though. The river is already started to go down."

"Ben Jordan," the man said with a great splurt, a costly effort, like somebody leaping over a stutter.

"I thought you'd recognize me, Joe."

"I never knew it was you, Ben. I thought it was one them Silases."

"Well I been telling you it was me."

"They's down here all the time choppin my trees and pullin down my fences. You know they burned me out, Ben. It was them done it."

"I heard about that," my father said.

"I didn't know it was you, Ben. I never knew it was you. I got this axe, I just take it along with me to give them a little scare. I wouldn't of if I'd known it was you. You come on up and see where I'm living now."

My father called me. "I got my young one out following me today."

"Well you and her both come up and get warm."

We followed this man, who still carried and carelessly swung his hatchet, up the slope and into the bush. The trees chilled the air, and underneath them was real snow, left over from winter, a foot, two feet deep. The tree trunks had rings around them, a curious dark space like the warmth you make with your breath.

We came out in a field of dead grass, and took a track across it to another, wider, field where there was something sticking out of the ground. It was a roof, slanting one way, not peaked, and out of the roof came a pipe with a cap on it, smoke blowing out. We went down the sort of steps that lead to a cellar, and that was what it was —a cellar with a roof on. My father said, "Looks like you fixed it up all right for yourself, Joe."

"It's warm. Being down in the ground the way it is, naturally it's warm. I thought what is the sense of building a house up again, they burned it down once, they'll burn it down again. What do I need a house for anyways? I got all the room I need here, I fixed it up comfortable." He opened the door at the bottom of the steps. "Mind your head here. I don't say everybody should live in a hole in the ground, Ben. Though animals do it, and what an animal does, by and large it makes sense. But if you're married, that's another story." He laughed. "Me, I don't plan on getting married."

It was not completely dark. There were the old cellar windows, letting in a little grimy light. The man lit a coal-oil lamp, though, and set it on the table.

"There, you can see where you're at."

It was all one room, an earth floor with boards not nailed together, just laid down to make broad paths for walking, a stove on a sort of platform, table, couch, chairs, even a kitchen cupboard, several thick, very dirty blankets of the type used in sleighs and to cover horses. Perhaps if it had not had such a terrible smell—of coal oil, urine, earth and stale heavy air—I would have recognized it as the sort of place I would like to live in myself, like the houses I made under snow drifts, in winter, with sticks of firewood for furniture, like another house I had made long ago under the veranda, my floor the strange powdery earth that never got sun or rain.

But I was wary, sitting on the dirty couch, pretending not to look at anything. My father said, "You're snug here, Joe, that's right." He sat by the table, and there the hatchet lay.

"You should of seen me before the snow started to melt. Wasn't nothing showing but a smokestack."

"Nor you don't get lonesome?"

"Not me. I was never one for lonesome. And I got a cat, Ben. Where is that cat? There he is, in behind the stove. He don't relish company, maybe." He pulled it out, a huge, gray tom with sullen eyes. "Show you what he can do." He took a saucer from the table and a Mason jar from the cupboard and poured something into the saucer. He set it in front of the cat.

"Joe that cat don't drink whiskey, does he?"

"You wait and see."

The cat rose and stretched himself stiffly, took one baleful look around and lowered his head to drink.

"Straight whiskey," my father said.

"I bet that's a sight you ain't seen before. And you ain't likely to see it again. That cat'd take whiskey ahead of milk any day. A matter of fact he don't get no milk, he's forgot what it's like. You want a drink, Ben?"

"Not knowing where you got that. I don't have a stomach like your cat."

The cat, having finished, walked sideways from the saucer, waited a moment, gave a clawing leap and landed unsteadily, but did not fall. It swayed, pawed the air a few times, meowing despairingly, then shot forward and slid under the end of the couch.

"Joe, you keep that up, you're not going to have a cat."

"It don't hurt him, he enjoys it. Let's see, what've we got for the little girl to eat?" Nothing, I hoped, but he brought a tin of Christmas candies, which seemed to have melted then hardened then melted again, so the colored stripes had run. They had a taste of nails.

"It's them Silases botherin me, Ben. They come by day and by night. People won't ever quit botherin me. I can hear them on the roof at night. Ben, you see them Silases you tell them what I got waitin for them." He picked up the hatchet and chopped down at the table, splitting the rotten oilcloth. "Got a shotgun too."

"Maybe they won't come and bother you no more, Joe."

The man groaned and shook his head. "They never will stop. No. They never will stop."

"Just try not paying any attention to them, they'll tire out and go away."

"They'll burn me in my bed. They tried to before."

My father said nothing, but tested the axe blade with his finger. Under the couch, the cat pawed and meowed in more and more feeble spasms of delusion. Overcome with tiredness, with warmth after cold, with bewilderment quite past bearing, I was falling asleep with my eyes open. My father set me down. "You're woken up now. Stand up. See. I can't carry you and this sack full of rats both."

We had come to the top of a long hill and that is where I woke. It was getting dark. The whole basin of country drained by the Wawanash River lay in front of us—greenish-brown smudge of bush with the leaves not out yet and evergreens, dark, shabby after winter, showing through, straw-brown fields and the others, darker from last year's plowing, with scales of snow faintly striping them (like the field we had walked across hours, hours earlier in the day) and the tiny fences and colonies of grey barns, and houses set apart, looking squat and small.

"Whose house is that?" my father said, pointing.

It was ours, I knew it after a minute. We had come around in a half-circle and there was the side of the house that nobody saw in winter, the front door that went unopened from November to April and was still stuffed with rags around its edges, to keep out the east wind.

"That's no more'n half a mile away and downhill. You can easy

walk home. Soon we'll see the light in the dining room where your
Momma is."

On the way I said, "Why did he have an axe?"

"Now listen," my father said. "Are you listening to me? He don't
mean any harm with that axe. It's just his habit, carrying it around.
But don't say anything about it at home. Don't mention it to your
Momma or Mary, either one. Because they might be scared about
it. You and me aren't, but they might be. And there is no use of
that."

After a while he said, "What are you not going to mention
about?" and I said, "The axe."

"You weren't scared, were you?"

"No," I said hopefully. "Who is going to burn him and his
bed?"

"Nobody. Less he manages it himself like he did last time."

"Who is the Silases?"

"Nobody," my father said. "Just nobody."

"We found the one for you today, Mary. Oh, I wisht we could've
brought him home."

"We thought you'd fell in the Wawanash River," said Mary
McQuade furiously, ungently pulling off my boots and my wet
socks.

"Old Joe Phippen that lives up in no man's land beyond the
bush."

"Him!" said Mary like an explosion. "He's the one burned his
house down, I know him!"

"That's right, and now he gets along fine without it. Lives in a
hole in the ground. You'd be as cosy as a groundhog, Mary."

"I bet he lives in his own dirt, all right." She served my father his
supper and he told her the story of Joe Phippen, the roofed cellar,
the boards across the dirt floor. He left out the axe but not the
whiskey and the cat. For Mary, that was enough.

"A man that'd do a thing like that ought to be locked up."

"Maybe so," my father said. "Just the same I hope they don't get
him for a while yet. Old Joe."

"Eat your supper," Mary said, bending over me. I did not for
some time realize that I was no longer afraid of her. "Look at her,"

she said. "Her eyes dropping out of her head, all she's been and seen. Was he feeding the whiskey to her too?"

"Not a drop," said my father, and looked steadily down the table at me. Like the children in fairy stories who have seen their parents make pacts with terrifying strangers, who have discovered that our fears are based on nothing but the truth, but who come back fresh from marvellous escapes and take up their knives and forks, with humility and good manners, prepared to live happily ever after—like them, dazed and powerful with secrets, I never said a word.

Responding

1. Describe the relationship the narrator has with a) her mother b) her father c) Mary McQuade.

2. What feelings most concern the narrator at the start of the story? How is she changed by her visit with Joe? Explain.

3. List the characters and note the images the narrator uses in describing each one. What do the images reveal about the characters?

4. What are the advantages in telling the story from the first-person point of view?

5. When we are children, certain experiences help us to mature or grow by giving us a better understanding of ourselves and others. Tell about one experience you had that helped you mature or grow in understanding.

6. Each of us can recall when, as children, we met an unusual and memorable character. Describe one memorable individual you recall from your own childhood. What were your feelings toward that person? Why?

Student notes, page 247

Jane Rule

A TELEVISION DRAMA

Carolee Mitchell's household routine is disrupted by a violent event that she might have ignored, if it had been just another distant news story. But this is for real . . .

*A*t one-thirty in the afternoon, Carolee Mitchell was running the vacuum cleaner, or she would have heard the first sirens and looked out. After the first, there weren't any others. The calling voices, even the number of dogs barking, could have been students on their way back to school, high-spirited in the bright, cold earliness of the year. Thinking back on the sounds, Carolee remembered a number of car doors being slammed, that swallow of air and report which made her smooth her hair automatically even if she wasn't expecting anyone. But what caught her eye finally was what always caught her eye: the flight of a bird from a treetop in the ravine out over the fringe of trees at the bottom of her steeply sloping front lawn, nearly private in the summer, exposed now to the startling activity of the street.

Three police cars were parked in front of the house, a motorcycle like a slanted stress in the middle of the intersection, half a dozen more police cars scattered up and down the two blocks. There were men in uniform up on her neighbor's terrace with rifles and field glasses. Police with dogs were crossing the empty field at the bottom of the ravine. More cars were arriving, police and reporters with cameras and sound equipment. Mingling among the uniforms

and equipment were the neighbors: Mrs. Rolston from the house across the street who had obviously not taken time to put on a coat and was rubbing her arms absent-mindedly as she stood and talked. Jane Carey from next door with a scarf tied round her head and what looked like one of her son's jackets thrown over her shoulders, old Mr. Monkson, a few small children. Cars and people kept arriving. Suddenly there was a voice magnified to reach even Carolee, surprised and unbelieving behind her picture window.

"Clear the street. All householders return to or stay in your houses. Clear the street."

Mrs. Rolston considered the idea for a moment but did not go in. The others paid no attention at all. Carolee wondered if she should go out just to find out what on earth was going on. Perhaps she should telephone someone, but everyone she might phone was already in the street. Was it a gas main? Not with all those dogs. A murder? It seemed unlikely that anyone would kill anyone else on this street, where every child had his own bedroom and most men either studies or basement workshops to retreat into. In any case, it was the middle of the afternoon. Mrs. Cole had come out on her balcony with field glasses focussed on the place where the dogs and police had entered the ravine. Field glasses. Where were Pete's field glasses? Carolee thought she knew, but she did not move to get them. She would not know what she was looking for in the undergrowth or the gardens.

"Clear the street. All householders return to or stay in your houses."

Police radios were now competing with each other. "Suspect last apprehended in the alley between . . ." "House to house search . . ." "Ambulance . . ."

If one of those policemen standing about on the street would come to search the house, Carolee could at least find out what was going on. Was that a T.V. crew? Dogs were barking in the ravine. Did police dogs bark? Nobody on the street seemed to be doing anything, except for the motorcycle policeman who was turning away some cars. Maybe Carolee should go empty the dishwasher and then come back. It was pointless to stand here by the window. Nothing was happening, or, if something was happening, Carolee couldn't see the point of it. She went to the window in Pete's study to see if she could discover activity on the side street. There were more policemen, and far up the block an ambulance was pulling away without a siren, its red light slowly circling. Carolee watched it until it turned the corner at the top of the hill. Then she turned back toward the sound of barking dogs and radios, but paused as she turned.

There, sitting against the curve of the laurel hedge by the lily pond, was a man, quite a young man, his head down, his left hand against his right shoulder. He was sick or hurt or dead. Or not really there at all, something Carolee's imagination had put there to explain the activity in the street, part of a collage, like an unlikely photograph in the middle of a painting. But he raised his head slightly then, and Carolee saw the blood on his jacket and trousers.

"I must call the police," she said aloud, but how could she call the police when they were already there, three of them standing not seventy feet away, just below the trees on the parking strip? She must call someone, but all the neighbors were still out of doors. And what if the police did discover him? He might be shot instead of helped. Carolee wanted to help him, whoever he was. It was such an odd way he was sitting, his legs stretched out in front of him so that he couldn't possibly have moved quickly. He might not be able to move at all. But she couldn't get to him, not without being seen. Suddenly he got to his feet, his left hand still against his right shoulder and also holding the lower part of his ducked face. He walked to the end of the curve of hedge as if it was very difficult for him to move, and then he began a stumbling run across the front lawn, through the trees, and out onto the parking strip. There he turned, hesitated, and fell on his back. Carolee had heard no shot. Now her view was blocked by a gathering of police and reporters, drawn to that new center like leaves to a central drain.

"Suspect apprehended on . . ."

What had he done? What had that hurt and stumbling boy done? Carolee was standing with her hand on the transistor radio before it occurred to her to turn it on.

"We interrupt this program with a news bulletin. A suspect has been apprehended on . . ."

He had robbed a bank, run a car into a tree, shot a policeman, been shot at.

"And now, here is our reporter on the scene."

140

Carolee could see the reporter quite clearly, standing in the street in front of the house, but she could hear only the radio voice, explaining what had happened.

"And now the ambulance is arriving . . ." as indeed it was. "The suspect, suffering from at least three wounds, who seems near death, is being lifted onto a stretcher . . ." This she couldn't see. It seemed to take a very long time before police cleared a path for the ambulance, again silent, its red light circling, to move slowly down the block and out of sight.

A newspaper reporter was walking up the front path, but Carolee didn't answer the door. She stood quietly away from the window and waited until he was gone. Then she went to the kitchen and began to empty the dishwasher. It was two o'clock. She turned on the radio again to listen to the regular news report. The details were the same. At three o'clock the hospital had reported that the policeman was in the operating room having a bullet removed from his right lung. At four o'clock the suspect was reported in only fair condition from wounds in the shoulder, jaw, leg and hand.

At five o'clock Pete came home, the evening paper in his hand. "Well, you've had quite a day," he said. "Are you all right?"

"Yes," Carolee said, her hands against his cold jacket, her cheek against his cold face. "Yes, I'm all right. What did the paper say?"

"It's all diagrams," he said, holding out the front page to her.

There was a map of the whole neighborhood, a sketched aerial map, a view of the roof of their house Carolee had never had. She followed the dots and arrows to the hood of a car crumpled under a flower of foliage, on again across the ravine, up their side hill, and there was the laurel hedge and the jelly bean lily pond, but the dots didn't stop there, arced round rather and immediately down through the trees to a fallen doll, all alone, not a policeman or reporter in sight, lying there exposed to nothing but a God's-eye view.

"You must have seen him," Pete said.

"Yes," Carolee agreed, still looking down on the rooftops of all her neighbours' houses.

"Did it frighten you?" Pete asked.

"Not exactly. It was hard to believe, and everything seemed to happen so very slowly."

"Did you get a good look at him?"

"I guess not really," Carolee said. Had he sat there by the laurel hedge at all, his long, stiff legs stretched out in front of him? The map didn't show it.

"Something has got to be done about all this violence," Pete said.

His tone and the look on his face made Carolee realize that Pete had been frightened, much more frightened than she was. Those dotted lines across his front lawn, that figure alone in the landscape —Carolee felt herself shaken by a new fear, looking at what Pete had seen.

"I'll get us a drink," Pete said.

Once they sat down, Carolee tried to tell her husband what it had been like, all those women just standing out in the street. She told him about the guns and field glasses and dogs and cameras. She did not tell him about the man, hurt, by the laurel hedge.

Pete turned on the television, and they watched three minutes of fast-moving images, first the policeman lifted into an ambulance, then officers and dogs running through the field, finally glimpses of the suspect on the ground and then shifted onto a stretcher; and, while they watched, a voice told them of the robbery, the chase, the capture. Finally several people were quickly interviewed, saying such things as, "I saw him go over the fence" or "He fell practically at my feet." That was Mrs. Rolston, still rubbing her cold arms in the winter day.

"I'm glad you had the good sense to stay inside," Pete said. He was holding her hand, beginning to relax into indignation and relief.

Carolee wasn't there, nor was the man there. If she had spoken to that reporter, if she had said then, "I saw him. He was sitting by the laurel hedge," would the dots in the paper have changed? Would the cameras have climbed into their nearly exposed winter garden? Would she believe now what she couldn't quite believe even then, that she stood at that window and saw a man dying in her garden?

Now a labor union boss was talking, explaining the unfair practices of the compensation board. Nearly at once, young marines were running, firing, falling. Planes were dropping bombs. Carolee wasn't there, but it seemed real to her, terribly real, so that for a moment she forgot Pete's hand in hers, her safe house on a safe street, and was afraid.

Responding

1. How does Carolee react when she first notices the activity in her neighborhood? How does she feel when she sees the wounded man in her yard? Support your answers with references to the story.

2. How, by comparison, does Carolee feel at the end of the story? Are her reactions believable? Why or why not?

3. Has the experience of that day changed Carolee Mitchell in a lasting way? Comment.

4. Find examples of references the author makes to news-gathering and news reporting. Why are the media emphasized so strongly? What point does the story make about how most people respond to media reports of violent events?

5. The next day, one of Carolee's neighbors calls to chat about what happened. Improvise the conversation that might take place.

6. Because most violent or tragic events occur at a distance, people in our society often do not become concerned or involved. What must happen for people to pay attention and offer help to victims of tragic circumstances such as widespread starvation or disease?

Student notes, page 247

Morley Callaghan

THE SENTIMENTALISTS

A downtown department store. A store detective watches three women customers. Two bored young men make a bet with each other: Which of the three is really *the thief?*

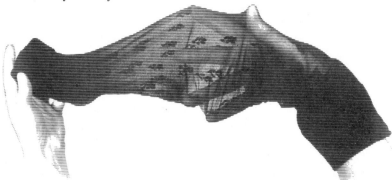

*I*t was at the scarf counter at noontime that Jack Malone, the young law student, saw the yellow scarf on the rack and thought he might give it to his girl for her birthday. His plump friend, Fred Webster, bored with wandering around from counter to counter in the department store, had just said, "Sure she'll like it. Take it," when a gray-haired woman in a blue sailor hat came gliding round the corner and bumped into Malone.

"Excuse me, lady," he said, but she was in his way, idly toying with the yellow scarf. "Excuse me, madam," he said firmly. Moving a step away, she said impatiently, "Excuse me," and went on fussing with the scarves without actually looking at them, and when the salesgirl approached she didn't look up. Reddening, the salesgirl retreated quickly, leaving her there peering through the screen of scarves at the silk-stocking counter in the next aisle.

"Why get sore? She's the store detective. You got in her way," Webster said.

"Why shouldn't I? I don't work for her."

"It's someone at the silk-stocking counter," Webster said, brightening. "Let's watch."

Because they were having a sale, silk stockings were out loose on the counter and sometimes there was a line of women and sometimes the line thinned out.

"If you were a betting man, who would you say it was?" Webster asked. He knew Malone was proud of his judgment of people and of the experience he got from talking to crooks of all kinds in the law office and in the police court. "I'll bet you five bucks," Webster said. "Go ahead, look over the field."

"It's too easy," Malone said. All he had to do was watch the detective behind the scarves and follow the direction of her eyes, watching three women at the end of the silk-stocking counter who had been standing there longer than the others. It was hard to get more than a glimpse of their faces, but one was a stout woman with a silver-fox fur and a dark, heavy, aggressive, and arrogant face. She looked very shrewd and competent. Her lips were heavy and greedy. If she were going to steal anything it would probably be something very valuable, and she wouldn't give it up easily. On the left of her was a lanky schoolgirl with no shape at all, a brainless-looking kid. And there was a young girl in a red felt hat and a fawn-colored loose spring coat.

All the women at the counter seemed to be sliding stockings over the backs of their hands and holding them up to the light. Getting a little closer, his excitement quickening, Malone tried to see into their faces and into their lives, and the first one he counted out was the girl in the fawn coat: she seemed like someone he had met on a train, or someone he had known all his life without ever knowing her name. In a hundred places they might have seen each other, at summer dances or on the streets where he had played when he was a kid. But while he was watching her and feeling sure of her, the schoolgirl sighed and dropped the stocking she was looking at and walked away.

"That leaves only the two," Webster whispered, coming alongside. His plump, good-natured face was disturbed, as if he, too, had decided the stout woman was far too sensible-looking to be a store thief, and his estimate of the girl in the fawn coat with the dark hair and the brown eyes was the same as Malone's. "I was thinking it would be the school kid doing something crazy," he whispered.

"So was I."

While they stood together, suddenly disturbed, the stout woman made a purchase and walked away slowly, opening her purse. They both turned, watching the bright-colored bank of scarves, and Malone suddenly longed to see the blue sailor hat go gliding behind the scarves, following the stout woman. But the detective was still there, waiting. You could see the motionless rim of her hat.

"Well, it's the girl in the fawn coat she's watching," Webster said.

"And what do you think?"

"I think the detective's crazy."

"Yet she's the one the woman's watching."

"Listen, I'll bet you that five bucks old eagle eye hiding over there is absolutely wrong about her."

"Not on your life. That's no bet. That kid's no thief," Malone said.

It wasn't just that the girl was pretty. But in the slow way she turned her head, swinging the dark hair over her raised collar, in the light of intelligence that shone in her dark eyes when she looked up quickly, and in the warmth that would surely come easily in her face, Malone was reminded that she might be someone like his own sister. Her clothes were not expensive: the fawn coat looked as if it had been worn at least three seasons. But his sister had looked like that the time they were all scrimping and saving to send her to college. Suddenly, Malone and Webster were joined, betting against the judgment of the store detective. They wanted to root for the girl, root her away from the counter. With a passionate eagerness to see the woman detective frustrated, Malone muttered in her direction, "Lady, you're picking on the wrong party. Just stick around a while and watch her walk away."

But the store detective's blue sailor hat was moving slowly, coming around, closing in. Yet the girl stood motionless. A stocking was in her hand, or her hand was on the counter, and her absentminded stillness, her lowered head—it became apparent—were a furtive awareness of the position of the salesgirl. Malone went to speak to Webster, and then he couldn't: they were both unbelieving and hurt. Yet there still was a chance. It became a desperate necessity that he should be right about the girl. "Go away, kid," he was begging her. "Why do you stand there looking like that? You're no thief. You're a kid. Get moving, why don't you?" But she bent her head, she hunched up her shoulders a little, and her hand on the counter was drawing a pair of silk stockings into the wide sleeve of her coat. As the store detective came slowly around the end of the scarf counter, Webster said, disgusted, "Just another little store thief."

Malone wanted to slap the girl and abuse her. It wasn't just that she had let him down, she seemed to have betrayed so many things that belonged to the most intimate and warmest part of his life. "Let her arrest her, what do we care?" he said as the store detective went slowly down the aisle. But in spite of himself he thought he would cry out if he stood there. He got excited. He walked along the aisle alone, taking out his watch as if he had been waiting a long time for someone. When he was opposite the girl he stopped, staring at her back, at the bunch of black curls under the rim of her hat, and he was sick and hesitant and bewildered. "Why, Helen," he said, reaching out and touching her, "have you been here all this time?" A wide, forced smile was on his face.

"Smile, please smile," he whispered, because he could see the store detective watching them. "Come away," he begged her. "They're watching you."

Before the scared smile came on her face, the silk stockings rolled in a ball in her palm and half up her sleeve were dropped almost naturally on the counter. She made it look like a careless gesture. "Hello," she said, "I was . . ." then her voice was lost. If he had not moved she would have stood gaping and incredulous, but he was scared for himself now, for he might be arrested as an accomplice, and he linked his arm under hers and started to walk down the aisle to the door.

They had to pass the store detective, and maybe it was because Malone instinctively tightened his hold on the girl's arm that he could feel it trembling. But the store detective, frustrated and puzzled, seemed to smile cynically just as they passed; he hated her for being right about the girl.

When they got outside, they stopped a moment under the big clock. It had been raining out, but there was bright sunlight on the wet pavements and the noonday crowd surged by. In that bright light, as he stood hesitating and the girl's head was lowered in humiliation, he noticed that there seemed to be a hundred little spots on her light coat, maybe rain marks or dust and rain. His heart was pounding, but now that he had got her safely out of the store, he wanted to get rid of her, and he didn't want her to offer any of that servile gratitude he got from petty thieves he helped in the police court.

"Thanks," she whispered.

"Forget it," he said, as if the whole thing had been nothing to him and he had understood from the beginning what she was. "I guess you'd better be getting on your way."

"All right."

"Well, there's no use standing here. Aren't you going along?"

"It doesn't matter," she said, standing there staring at him, her face still full of humiliation.

"You better be heading somewhere out of here. Where are you from?" he asked awkwardly.

"Out of town," she said. Then she touched him on the arm. "Listen, what was the idea?" she asked. While she waited for him to answer her face seemed to brighten. She was looking at him, looking right into his eyes. "Why did you do it? What's it to you?" They seemed to be alone on the street while she waited breathlessly because she had been offered some incredible promise, a turn that gave her a wild hope.

"We were standing there watching," he said uneasily, as he nodded to Webster who had followed them out and was now standing by the window trying to hear what she said. "Me and my pal, we saw what was going on," Malone said. Then, remembering their disappointment, he said bluntly, "We were betting on you."

"How do you mean?"

"When we saw the detective watching you—"

"Yes . . ."

"Our money went on you . . . that she was wrong . . . You let us down, that's all; we were wrong. We lose."

"Oh," she said, startled. As Webster came closer, she swung her head in wild resentment at him. Again they were both staring at her, watching her. She looked around the street at the faces of passing people as if everybody had suddenly stopped to watch her and make a little bet. "A buck she will, a buck she won't, eh!" she said as her eyes brightened with a crazy fury. "Get out of my way," she whispered. Swinging her foot she kicked him savagely on the shin.

As he felt the pain he could think only of how she had asked, "Why did you do it?" and waited breathlessly for some gesture from him. At that moment there did not seem to be a single good instinct, a single good thing in his life that he had not betrayed.

And she came walking right at him as if she would walk right through him if he did not step aside, and she had her head up and her fists clenched tight, going down the street, going deeper into the crowd with the sun touching her red hat and her good legs with the runs down her stockings.

Responding

1. Why is Jack Malone so disappointed when the girl turns out to be a thief? What motivates him to go down the aisle and rescue her?

2. Explain what you think is going through the girl's mind as she waits for Jack to answer her question about why he rescued her. How does she react to Jack's answer? Why?

3. What are Jack's feelings after the girl kicks him in the shin? Explain why he felt that "there did not seem to be a single good instinct, a single good thing in his life that he had not betrayed."

4. How much do we learn about the thoughts and feelings of each character in the story? Why do you think the author chose to write the story this way?

5. Continue the story, adding a dialogue that takes place as Jack chases after and stops the girl. What would he say? How would she likely answer?

Student notes, page 248

6 THEME AND MEANING

Why do readers and listeners find stories so appealing? If asked that question, most of us would answer that stories are entertaining. This is true—for centuries, human beings have enjoyed being drawn into the absorbing world of literature.

Most people can recall childhood stories that caused them to worry about the fate of a beautiful princess, to tremble at the thought of ogres hiding under a bridge, or to cheer when the evil wolf was finally defeated. As children grow older, they usually become more absorbed by the mysteries that need unravelling, superheroes that fight against seemingly impossible odds, or young people like themselves who are fighting injustice. And as they continue to grow older, their tastes change, though they still love a good, entertaining story.

Short stories offer more than entertainment, however. Many short stories provide insights into what world is like and why human beings behave as they do. These insights or truths are the themes of stories.

The three selections in this chapter provide excellent examples of stories that entertain—some more than others—and that also have insights or truths to communicate. The first story, "The Witch," shocks readers when it takes an unexpected turn from peacefulness to violence, and leaves us with some disturbing thoughts about human nature. The second story, "Dr. Heidegger's Experiment," shows us the thoughts and feelings of a doctor and his aged friends as they experiment with water from the Fountain of Youth. Because we see into each character, the purpose of the story becomes clear to us: given a second chance, many people still would not change their ways. The third, "The Old Woman," encourages us to think about the problems and fears associated with aging.

These three stories have significant themes to consider. Stories such as these are important because they awaken understanding that otherwise might never have been gained.

Shirley Jackson

THE WITCH

A family's quiet train ride is interrupted by a visit from a mysterious stranger. Could this man be a witch?

The coach was so nearly empty that the little boy had a seat all to himself, and his mother sat across the aisle on the seat next to the little boy's sister, a baby with a piece of toast in one hand and a rattle in the other. She was strapped securely to the seat so she could sit up and look around, and whenever she began to slip slowly sideways the strap caught her and held her halfway until her mother turned around and straightened her again. The little boy was looking out the window and eating a cookie, and the mother was reading quietly, answering the little boy's questions without looking up.

"We're on a river," the little boy said. "This is a river and we're on it."

"Fine," his mother said.

"We're on a bridge over a river," the little boy said to himself.

The few other people in the coach were sitting at the other end of the car; if any of them had occasion to come down the aisle the little boy would look around and say, "Hi," and the stranger would usually say, "Hi," back and sometimes ask the little boy if he were enjoying the train ride, or even tell him he was a fine big fellow. These comments annoyed the little boy and he would turn irritably back to the window.

"There's a cow," he would say, or, sighing, "How far do we have to go?"

"Not much longer now," his mother said, each time.

Once the baby, who was very quiet and busy with her rattle and her toast, which the mother would renew constantly, fell over too far sideways and banged her head. She began to cry, and for a minute there was noise and movement around the mother's seat. The little boy slid down from his own seat and ran across the aisle to pet his sister's feet and beg her not to cry, and finally the baby laughed and went back to her toast, and the little boy received a lollipop from his mother and went back to the window.

"I saw a witch," he said to his mother after a minute. "There was a big old ugly old bad old witch outside."

"Fine," his mother said.

"A big old ugly witch and I told her to go away and she went away," the little boy went on, in a quiet narrative to himself, "she came and said, 'I'm going to eat you up,' and I said, 'no, you're not,' and I chased her away, the bad old mean witch."

He stopped talking and looked up as the outside door of the coach opened and a man came in. He was an elderly man, with a pleasant face under white hair; his blue suit was only faintly touched by the disarray that comes from a long train trip. He was carrying a cigar, and when the little boy said, "Hi," the man gestured at him with the cigar and said, "Hello yourself, son." He stopped just beside the little boy's seat, and leaned against the back, looking down at the little boy, who craned his neck to look upward. "What you looking for out that window?" the man asked.

"Witches," the little boy said promptly. "Bad old mean witches."

"I see," the man said. "Find many?"

"My father smokes cigars," the little boy said.

"All men smoke cigars," the man said. "Someday you'll smoke a cigar, too."

"I'm a man already," the little boy said.

"How old are you?" the man asked.

The little boy, at the eternal question, looked at the man suspiciously for a minute and then said, "Twenty-six. Eight hunnerd and forty eighty."

His mother lifted her head from the book. "Four," she said, smiling fondly at the little boy.

"Is that so?" the man said politely to the little boy. "Twenty-six." He nodded his head at the mother across the aisle. "Is that your mother?"

The little boy leaned forward to look and then said, "Yes, that's her."

"What's your name?" the man asked.

The little boy looked suspicious again. "Mr. Jesus," he said.

"*Johnny*," the little boy's mother said. She caught the little boy's eye and frowned deeply.

"That's my sister over there," the little boy said to the man. "She's twelve-and-a-half."

"Do you love your sister?" the man asked. The little boy stared, and the man came around the side of the seat and sat down next to the little boy. "Listen," the man said, "shall I tell you about my little sister?"

The mother, who had looked up anxiously when the man sat down next to her little boy, went peacefully back to her book.

"Tell me about your sister," the little boy said. "Was she a witch?"

"Maybe," the man said.

The little boy laughed excitedly, and the man leaned back and puffed at his cigar. "Once upon a time," he began. "I had a little sister, just like yours." The little boy looked up at the man, nodding at every word. "My little sister," the man went on, "was so pretty and so nice that I loved her more than anything else in the world. So shall I tell you what I did?"

The little boy nodded more vehemently, and the mother lifted her eyes from her book and smiled, listening.

"I bought her a rocking-horse and a doll and a million lollipops," the man said, "and then I took her and I put my hands around her neck and I pinched her and I pinched her until she was dead."

The little boy gasped and the mother turned around, her smile fading. She opened her mouth, and then closed it again as the man went on. "And then I took and I cut her head off and I took her head—"

"Did you cut her all in pieces?" the little boy asked breathlessly.

"I cut off her head and her hands and her feet and her hair and her nose," the man said, "and I hit her with a stick and I killed her."

"Wait a minute," the mother said, but the baby fell over sideways just at that minute and by the time the mother had set her up again the man was going on.

"And I took her head and I pulled out all her hair and—"

"Your little *sister*?" the little boy prompted eagerly.

"My little sister," the man said firmly. "And I put her head in a cage with a bear and the bear ate it all up."

"Ate her *head* all up?" the little boy asked.

The mother put her book down and came across the aisle. She stood next to the man and said, "Just what do you think you're doing." The man looked up courteously and she said, "Get out of here."

"Did I frighten you?" the man said. He looked down at the little boy and nudged with an elbow and he and the little boy laughed.

"This man cut up his little sister," the little boy said to his mother.

"I can very easily call the conductor," the mother said to the man.

"The conductor will *eat* my mommy," the little boy said. "We'll chop her head off."

"And little sister's head, too," the man said. He stood up, and the mother stood back to let him get out of the seat. "Don't ever come back in this car," she said.

"My mommy will eat *you*," the little boy said to the man.

The man laughed, and the little boy laughed, and then the man said, "Excuse me," to the mother and went past her out of the car. When the door had closed behind him the little boy said, "How much longer do we have to stay on this old train?"

"Not much longer," the mother said. She stood looking at the little boy, wanting to say something, and finally she said, "You sit still and be a good boy. You may have another lollipop."

The little boy climbed down eagerly and followed his mother back to her seat. She took a lollipop from a bag in her pocketbook and gave it to him. "What do you say?" she asked.

"Thank you," the little boy said. "Did that man really cut his little sister up in pieces?"

"He was just teasing," the mother said, and added urgently, "Just *teasing*."

"Prob'ly," the little boy said. With his lollipop he went back to his own seat, and settled himself to look out the window again. "Prob'ly he was a witch."

Responding

1. Contrast the way in which the mother and the man treat the little boy. Support your answer with examples from the story.

2. (a) What do you think is the man's motivation in telling the little boy such a shocking story?
   (b) How does the little boy react to the story?

3. Is the mother's anger at the man justifiable, or does she overreact to his story? Comment.

4. What do witches represent to the little boy? How does he react when he thinks he sees a witch outside the window? Why does the little boy think the man was a witch?

5. What does the story have to say about the nature of children and the nature of human beings?

6. The man's story is extremely violent, yet the little boy reacts with excitement and interest. List three examples of children's poems or stories that are particularly violent. Do you think this sort of literature should be kept away from children? Why or why not?

7. Over the last decade, some violent horror stories have been popular in the movies. Why, in your view, do so many people enjoy horror stories?

Student notes, page 248

Nathaniel Hawthorne

DR. HEIDEGGER'S EXPERIMENT

Dr. Heidegger has invited four old friends to his study to assist him in an unusual experiment. The drinks are on the host tonight—water from the famed Fountain of Youth!

*T*hat very singular man, old Dr. Heidegger, once invited four venerable friends to meet him in his study. There were three white-bearded gentlemen, Mr. Medbourne, Colonel Killigrew, and Mr. Gascoigne, and a withered gentlewoman, whose name was the Widow Wycherly. They were all melancholy old creatures, who had been unfortunate in life, and whose greatest misfortune it was that they were not long ago in their graves. Mr. Medbourne, in the vigor of his age, had been a prosperous merchant, but had lost his all by a frantic speculation, and was now little better than a mendicant. Colonel Killigrew had wasted his best years, and his health and substance, in the pursuit of sinful pleasures which had given birth to a brood of pains, such as the gout, and diverse other torments of soul and body. Mr. Gascoigne was a ruined politician, a man of evil fame, or at least had been so, till time had buried him from the knowledge of the present generation, and made him obscure instead of infamous. As for the Widow Wycherly, tradition tells us that she was a great beauty in her day; but, for a long while past, she had

lived in deep seclusion, on account of certain scandalous stories which had prejudiced the gentry of the town against her. It is a circumstance worth mentioning, that each of these three old gentlemen, Mr. Medbourne, Colonel Killigrew, and Mr. Gascoigne, were early lovers of the Widow Wycherly, and had once been on the point of cutting each other's throats for her sake. And before proceeding farther, I will merely hint that Dr. Heidegger and all his four guests were sometimes thought to be a little beside themselves; as is not unfrequently the case with old people, when worried either by present troubles or woeful recollections.

"My dear old friends," said Dr. Heidegger, motioning them to be seated, "I am desirous of your assistance in one of those little experiments with which I amuse myself here in my study."

If all stories were true, Dr. Heidegger's study must have been a very curious place. It was a dim, old-fashioned chamber, festooned with cobwebs, and besprinkled with antique dust. Around the walls stood several oaken bookcases, the lower shelves of which were filled with rows of gigantic folios and black-letter quartos, and the upper with little parchment-covered duodecimos. Over the central bookcase was a bronze bust of Hippocrates, with which, according to some authorities, Dr. Heidegger was accustomed to hold consultations in all difficult cases of his practice. In the obscurest corner of the room stood a tall and narrow oaken closet, with its door ajar, within which doubtfully appeared a skeleton. Between two of the bookcases hung a looking glass, presenting its high and dusty plate within a tarnished gilt frame. Among many wonderful stories related of this mirror, it was fabled that the spirits of all the doctor's deceased patients dwelt within its verge, and would stare him in the face whenever he looked thitherward. The opposite side of the chamber was ornamented with the full-length portrait of a young lady, arrayed in the faded magnificence of silk, satin, and brocade, and with a visage as faded as her dress. Above half a century ago, Dr. Heidegger had been on the point of marriage with this young lady; but, being affected with some slight disorder, she had swallowed one of her lover's prescriptions, and died on the bridal evening. The greatest curiosity of the study remains to be mentioned; it was a ponderous folio volume, bound in black leather, with massive silver clasps. There were no letters on the back, and nobody could tell the title of the book. But it was well-known to be a book of magic; and once, when a chambermaid had lifted it, merely to brush away the dust, the skeleton had rattled in its closet, the picture of the young lady had stepped one foot upon the floor, and several ghastly faces had peeped forth from the mirror; while the brazen head of Hippocrates frowned, and said—"Forbear!"

Such was Dr. Heidegger's study. On the summer afternoon of our tale, a small round table, as black as ebony, stood in the center of the room, sustaining a cut-glass vase of beautiful form and elaborate workmanship. The sunshine came through the window, between the heavy festoons of two faded damask curtains, and fell directly across this vase; so that a mild splendor was reflected from it on the ashen visages of the five old people who sat around. Four champagne glasses were also on the table.

"My dear old friends," repeated Dr. Heidegger, "may I reckon on your aid in performing an exceedingly curious experiment?"

Now Dr. Heidegger was a very strange old gentleman, whose eccentricity had become the nucleus for a thousand fantastic stories. Some of these fables, to my shame be it spoken, might possibly be traced back to mine own veracious self; and if any passages of the present tale should startle the reader's faith, I must be content to bear the stigma of a fiction-monger.

When the doctor's four guests heard him talk of his proposed experiment, they anticipated nothing more wonderful than the murder of a mouse in an air pump, or the examination of a cobweb by the microscope, or some similar nonsense, with which he was constantly in the habit of pestering his intimates. But without waiting for a reply, Dr. Heidegger hobbled across the chamber, and returned with the same ponderous folio, bound in black leather, which common report affirmed to be a book of magic. Undoing the silver clasps, he opened the volume, and took from among its black-letter pages a rose, or what was once a rose, though now the green leaves and crimson petals had assumed one brownish hue, and the ancient flower seemed ready to crumble to dust in the doctor's hands.

"This rose," said Dr. Heidegger, with a sigh, "this same withered and crumbling flower, blossomed five and fifty years ago. It was given me by Sylvia Ward, whose portrait hangs yonder; and I meant to wear it in my bosom at our wedding. Five and fifty years it has been treasured between the leaves of this old volume. Now, would you deem it possible that this rose of half a century could ever bloom again?"

"Nonsense!" said the Widow Wycherly, with a peevish toss of her head. "You might as well ask whether an old woman's wrinkled face could ever bloom again."

"See!" answered Dr. Heidegger.

He uncovered the vase, and threw the faded rose into the water which it contained. At first it lay lightly on the surface of the fluid, appearing to imbibe none of its moisture. Soon, however, a singular change began to be visible. The crushed and dried petals stirred, and assumed a deepening tinge of crimson, as if the flower were reviving from a deathlike slumber; the slender stalk and twigs of foliage became green; and there was the rose of half a century, looking as fresh as when Sylvia Ward had first given it to her lover. It was scarcely full-blown; for some of its delicate red leaves curled modestly around its moist bosom, within which two or three dewdrops were sparkling.

"That is certainly a very pretty deception," said the doctor's friends; carelessly, however, for they had witnessed greater miracles at a conjurer's show; "pray how was it effected?"

"Did you never hear of the 'Fountain of Youth'?" asked Dr. Heidegger, "which Ponce de Leon, the Spanish adventurer, went in search of, two or three centuries ago?"

"But did Ponce de Leon ever find it?" said the Widow Wycherly.

"No," answered Dr. Heidegger, "for he never sought it in the right place. The famous Fountain of Youth, if I am rightly informed, is situated in the southern part of the Floridian peninsula, not far from Lake Macaco. Its source is overshadowed by several gigantic magnolias, which, though numberless centuries old, have been kept as fresh as violets by the virtues of this wonderful water. An acquaintance of mine, knowing my curiosity in such matters, has sent me what you see in the vase."

"Ahem!" said Colonel Killigrew, who believed not a word of the doctor's story; "and what may be the effect of this fluid on the human frame?"

"You shall judge for yourself, my dear colonel," replied Dr. Heidegger; "and all of you, my respected friends, are welcome to so much of this admirable fluid as may restore to you the bloom of youth. For my own part, having had much trouble in growing old, I am in no hurry to grow young again. With your permission, therefore, I will merely watch the progress of the experiment."

While he spoke, Dr. Heidegger had been filling the four champagne glasses with the water of the Fountain of Youth. It was apparently impregnated with an effervescent gas, for little bubbles were continually ascending from the depths of the glasses, and bursting in silvery spray at the surface. As the liquor diffused a pleasant perfume, the old people doubted not that it possessed cordial and comfortable properties; and, though utter skeptics as to its rejuvenescent power, they were inclined to swallow it at once. But Dr. Heidegger besought them to stay a moment.

"Before you drink, my respectable old friends," said he, "it would be well that, with the experience of a lifetime to direct you, you should draw up a few general rules for your guidance, in passing a second time through the perils of youth. Think what a sin and a shame it would be, if with your peculiar advantages, you should not become patterns of virtue and wisdom to all the young people of the age!"

The doctor's four venerable friends made him no answer, except by a feeble and tremulous laugh; so very ridiculous was the idea, that, knowing how closely repentance treads behind the steps of error, they should ever go astray again.

"Drink, then," said the doctor, bowing; "I rejoice that I have so well-selected the subjects of my experiment."

With palsied hands they raised the glasses to their lips. The liquor, if it really possessed such virtues as Dr. Heidegger imputed to it, could not have been bestowed on four human beings who needed it more woefully. They looked as if they had never known what youth or pleasure was, but had been the offspring of Nature's dotage, and always the gray, decrepit, sapless, miserable creatures, who now sat stooping round the doctor's table, without life enough in their souls or bodies to be animated even by the prospect of growing young again. They drank off the water, and replaced their glasses on the table.

Assuredly, there was an almost immediate improvement in the aspect of the party, not unlike what might have been produced by a glass of generous wine, together with a sudden glow of cheerful sunshine, brightening over all their visages at once. There was a healthful suffusion on their cheeks, instead of the ashen hue that had made them look so corpselike. They gazed at one another, and fancied that some magic power had really begun to smooth away the deep and sad inscription which Father Time had been so long engraving on their brows. The Widow Wycherly adjusted her cap, for she felt almost like a woman again.

"Give us more of this wondrous water!" cried they eagerly. "We are younger—but we are still too old! Quick—give us more!"

"Patience, patience!" quoth Dr. Heidegger, who sat watching the experiment with philosophic coolness. "You have been a long time growing old. Surely you might be content to grow young in half an hour! But the water is at your service."

Again he filled their glasses with the liquor of youth, enough of which still remained in the vase to turn half the old people in the city to the age of their own grandchildren. While the bubbles were yet sparkling on the brim, the doctor's four guests snatched their glasses from the table, and swallowed the contents at a single gulp. Was it delusion? Even while the draught was passing down their throats, it seemed to have wrought a change on their whole systems. Their eyes grew clear and bright; a dark shade deepened among their silvery locks; they sat around the table, three gentlemen of middle age, and a woman hardly beyond her buxom prime.

"My dear widow, you are charming!" cried Colonel Killigrew, whose eyes had been fixed upon her face, while the shadows of age were flitting from it like darkness from the crimson daybreak.

The fair widow knew, of old, that Colonel Killigrew's compliments were not always measured by sober truth; so she started up and ran to the mirror, still dreading that the ugly visage of an old woman would meet her gaze. Meanwhile, the three gentlemen behaved in such a manner as proved that the water of the Fountain of Youth possessed some intoxicating qualities; unless, indeed, their exhilaration of spirits were merely a lightsome dizziness, caused by the sudden removal of the weight of years. Mr. Gascoigne's mind seemed to run on political topics, but whether relating to the past, present, or future, could not easily be determined, since the same ideas and phrases have been in vogue these fifty years. Now he rattled forth full-throated sentences about patriotism, national glory, and the people's rights; now he muttered some perilous stuff or other, in a sly and doubtful whisper, so cautiously that even his own conscience could scarcely catch the secret; and now again he spoke in measured accents, and a deeply deferential tone, as if a royal ear were listening to his well-turned periods. Colonel Killigrew all this time had been trolling forth a jolly bottle song, and ringing his glass in symphony with the chorus, while his eyes wandered towards the buxom figure of the Widow Wycherly. On the other side of the table, Mr. Medbourne was involved in a calculation of dollars and cents, with which was strangely intermingled a project for supplying the East Indies with ice, by harnessing a team of whales to the polar icebergs.

As for the Widow Wycherly, she stood before the mirror curtsying and simpering to her own image, and greeting it as the friend whom she loved better than all the world beside. She thrust her face close to the glass, to see whether some long-remembered wrinkle or crow's-foot had indeed vanished. She examined whether the snow had so entirely melted from her hair, that the venerable cap could be safely thrown aside. At last, turning briskly away, she came with a sort of dancing step to the table.

"My dear old doctor," cried she, "pray favor me with another glass!"

"Certainly, my dear madam, certainly!" replied the complaisant doctor; "See! I have already filled the glasses."

There, in fact, stood the four glasses, brimful of this wonderful water, the delicate spray of which, as it effervesced from the surface, resembled the tremulous glitter of diamonds. It was now so nearly sunset that the chamber had grown duskier than ever; but a mild and moonlike splendor gleamed from within the vase, and rested alike on the four guests, and on the doctor's venerable figure. He sat in a high-backed, elaborately carved, oaken armchair, with a gray dignity of aspect that might have well befitted that very Father Time whose power had never been disputed save by this fortunate company. Even while quaffing the third draught of the Fountain of Youth, they were almost awed by the expression of his mysterious visage.

But, the next moment, the exhilarating gush of young life shot through their veins. They were now in the happy prime of youth. Age, with its miserable train of cares, and sorrows, and diseases, was remembered only as the trouble of a dream from which they had joyously awoke. The fresh gloss of the soul, so early lost, and without which the world's successive scenes had been but a gallery of faded pictures, again threw its enchantment over all their prospects. They felt like new-created beings, in a new-created universe.

"We are young! We are young!" they cried, exultingly.

Youth, like the extremity of age, had effaced the strongly marked characteristics of middle life, and mutually assimilated them all. They were a group of merry youngsters, almost maddened with the exuberant frolicsomeness of their years. The most singular effect of their gaiety was an impulse to mock the infirmity and decrepitude of which they had so lately been the victims. They laughed loudly at their old-fashioned attire, the wide-skirted coats and flapped waistcoats of the young men, and the ancient cap and gown of the blooming girl. One limped across the floor, like a gouty grandfather; one set a pair of spectacles astride of his nose, and pretended to pore over the black-letter pages of the book of magic; a third seated himself in an armchair, and strove to imitate the venerable dignity of Dr. Heidegger. Then all shouted mirthfully, and leaped about the room. The Widow Wycherly—if so fresh a damsel could be called a widow—tripped up to the doctor's chair, with a mischievous merriment in her rosy face.

"Doctor, you dear old soul," cried she, "get up and dance with me!" And then the four young people laughed louder than ever, to think what a queer figure the poor old doctor would cut.

"Pray excuse me," answered the doctor quietly. "I am old and rheumatic, and my dancing days were over long ago. But either of these young gentlemen will be glad of so pretty a partner."

"Dance with me, Clara!" cried Colonel Killigrew.

"No, no, I will be her partner!" shouted Mr. Gascoigne.

"She promised me her hand, fifty years ago!" exclaimed Mr. Medbourne.

They all gathered round her. One caught both her hands in his passionate grasp—another threw his arm about her waist—the third buried his hand among the glossy curls that clustered beneath the widow's cap. Blushing, panting, struggling, chiding, laughing, her warm breath fanning each of their faces by turns, she strove to disengage herself, yet still remained in their triple embrace. Never was there a livelier picture of youthful rivalship, with bewitching beauty for the prize. Yet, by a strange deception, owing to the duskiness of the chamber, and the antique dresses which they still wore, the tall mirror is said to have reflected the figures of the three old, gray, withered grandsires, ridiculously contending for the skinny ugliness of a shrivelled grandam.

But they were young: their burning passions proved them so. Inflamed to madness by the coquetry of the girl-widow, who neither granted nor quite withheld her favors, the three rivals began to interchange threatening glances. Still keeping hold of the fair prize, they grappled fiercely at one another's throats. As they struggled to and fro, the table was overturned, and the vase dashed into a thousand fragments. The precious Water of Youth flowed in a bright stream across the floor, moistening the wings of a butterfly, which, grown old in the decline of summer, had alighted there to die. The insect fluttered lightly through the chamber, and settled on the snowy head of Dr. Heidegger.

"Come, come, gentlemen!—come, Madam Wycherly," exclaimed the doctor, "I really must protest against this riot."

They stood still, and shivered; for it seemed as if gray Time were calling them back from their sunny youth, far down into the chill and darksome vale of years. They looked at old Dr. Heidegger, who sat in his carved armchair, holding the rose of half a century, which he had rescued from among the fragments of the shattered vase. At the motion of his hand, the four rioters resumed their seats; the more readily, because their violent exertions had wearied them, youthful though they were.

"My poor Sylvia's rose!" cried Dr. Heidegger, holding it in the light of the sunset clouds; "it appears to be fading again."

And so it was. Even while the party were looking at it, the flower continued to shrivel up, till it became as dry and fragile as when the doctor had first thrown it into the vase. He shook off the few drops of moisture which clung to its petals.

"I love it as well thus as in its dewy freshness," observed he, pressing the withered rose to his withered lips. While he spoke, the butterfly fluttered down from the doctor's snowy head, and fell upon the floor.

His guests shivered again. A strange chillness, whether of the body or spirit they could not tell, was creeping gradually over them all. They gazed at one another, and fancied that each fleeting moment snatched away a charm, and left a deepening furrow where none had been before. Was it an illusion? Had the changes of a lifetime been crowded into so brief a space, and were they now four aged people, sitting with their old friend, Dr. Heidegger?

"Are we grown old again, so soon?" cried they dolefully.

In truth, they had. The Water of Youth possessed merely a virtue more transient than that of wine. The delirium which it created had effervesced away. Yes! they were old again. With a shuddering impulse that showed her a woman still, the widow clasped her skinny hands before her face, and wished that the coffin lid were over it, since it could be no longer beautiful.

"Yes, friends, ye are old again," said Dr. Heidegger; "and lo! the Water of Youth is all lavished on the ground. Well—I bemoan it not; for if the fountain gushed at my very doorstep, I would not stoop to bathe my lips in it—no, though its delirium were for years instead of moments. Such is the lesson ye have taught me!"

But the doctor's four friends had taught no such lesson to themselves. They resolved forthwith to make a pilgrimage to Florida, and quaff at morning, noon, and night, from the Fountain of Youth.

Responding

1. According to Dr. Heidegger, what is the purpose of his experiment?

2. What do Dr. Heidegger's friends have in common? How does each of them behave during the experiment?

3. Why would Dr. Heidegger not stoop to bathe his lips in the Fountain of Youth? Do his friends feel the same way? Comment.

4. Who is the narrator of the story? Though he is not a participant in the experiment, the narrator relates all the details. How does he know what happened to the doctor and his friends? How certain of his facts is the narrator?

5. What points are made about youth and aging in the story? Do you agree with the views in the story? Comment.

6. Improvise a conversation in which Dr. Heidegger and his friends are interviewed on a talk show focussing on aging.

7. Some scientists hope to develop a vaccine against aging. They speculate that human beings could then live approximately 800 years. Do you feel this is desirable? Explain your answer.

Student notes, page 248

Elizabeth Brewster

THE OLD WOMAN

Florrie moves into a highrise apartment and is befriended by a lonely old woman. At first, the friendship is pleasant enough but then Florrie becomes uneasy . . .

1

*T*he old woman knew she was getting a new neighbor in the apartment across the hall from her. The apartment had been vacant for nearly two weeks. There had been a painter; she had peered in curiously and seen him sloshing a creamy white paint on the walls. There had been someone in to check the refrigerator and the stove. Then, this morning, the movers had come, a truck from out of town, and had brought up table, chairs, buffet, chesterfield, bed, a whole array of cardboard cartons filled with—what? dishes? The new tenant had come, too, in a taxi with suitcases, and had gone out again for a time, leaving the movers to put in the furniture by themselves. She was a woman of perhaps thirty-five or forty, the old woman decided, not a young girl. But no husband in evidence, so far as she could tell.

In the evening, when the old woman came out of her own apartment to put some garbage down the garbage chute, she could tell that the tenant had come in again because there was a bright light in the hall of the apartment shining visibly under the front door. Having got rid of the garbage, the old woman came back and stood in front of her neighbor's door. She would knock and give her a welcome, she decided.

The new tenant came to the door of the apartment, wearing an apron over her slacks. She was tall, thin, almost hollow-cheeked, with straight hair and brown eyes. She looked questioningly at the old woman. The floor of the small kitchen and of the dining area was crowded with boxes, some still full, some now empty, and masses of wrapping paper lay scattered about. Some dishes, some books, the old woman could see. "I just thought I'd say 'Yoo-hoo,'" the old woman said. "I'm Mrs. Cornish, your neighbor from across the hall. I saw the movers come with your things."

"Thank you, Mrs. Cornish," the woman said (not telling her own name, though). "I'd ask you in, but you can see what a mess the place is."

"Oh, well, another time. I used to be quite friendly with the boys who were here before."

"Boys? I thought the caretaker had said there was one man, an old bachelor."

"One? Oh, no, there were two of them—two boys. Well, I'll be off and leave you to your unpacking. Don't tire yourself."

Back in her own apartment, Mrs. Cornish stood in the kitchen looking around with perplexity. Had she done the errand she set out to do? Oh, yes, of course, she had emptied the garbage. That woman looked too thin—needed fattening up. Had there been only one tenant before? Maybe the boys had been earlier. Could that be? She did sometimes lose track of time.

She made her way, rather painfully because of her stiff right knee, into her living room, where she settled herself in her big leather armchair in front of the television. But she couldn't keep her mind on those TV antics. She picked up the newspaper, tried to read it. Too many obituaries, too many of them of people younger than herself. The cooking section was more cheerful. That's what she should do. Bake a batch of something—cookies? biscuits?—and take it across to the new tenant.

2

By the time the second knock came, Florrie Middleton was beginning to feel that she just might possibly manage to get the kitchen in order for breakfast tomorrow morning. The books could wait until tomorrow; as a matter of fact, it would be ages before they were really in order; but at least she could get them up off the floor and into bookcases. Now who could this be? Another neighbour? People sometimes said that highrises were unfriendly places, but this one didn't seem to be.

After all, it was the same old dear as before, Mrs. Cornish was it? A stocky, shapeless figure in a cotton house-dress, her feet thrust into slippers. Wisps of white hair were straggling out of her bun, forming an aureole effect around her pink face. This time she was carrying a mounded plate covered with a napkin.

"Sugar cookies," she said, beaming at Florrie and holding out the plate. "I knew you wouldn't have time to bake when you're unpacking."

"That's very kind of you. I'd better put these on another plate so you can have yours back."

"Oh, no, no," Mrs. Cornish cried, backing away. "Keep it until you've eaten the cookies. Then you can bring it back to me. That's my door right over there—see?"

Florrie didn't really like cookies, but it was good of the old dear to bring them. Breaking off a corner of one, she nibbled at it. Poor old biddy—she must've forgotten the salt. Thank goodness she didn't need to eat them before the old woman's eyes. She felt half guilty sneaking the cookies into the garbage later, and she had to guess a time that might seem reasonable for them to be eaten so that she could return the plate to Mrs. Cornish.

The old woman's apartment was full to bursting with furniture, much too much of it. Probably she hadn't been able to bear the thought of giving up the second china cabinet with all its little figurines, the extra coffee tables, the oak table which was just too big for the dining nook, the Victorian love seat crowded up next to the chesterfield. Florrie found her way past footstools and hassocks to a chair (for of course the old woman would not allow her to leave without a cup of tea and a piece of her lemon bread, just freshly made).

"I know your name now," the old woman said, "from the card on your door. F.J. Middleton. Is it Miss or Mrs.?"

"Florrie Middleton. I'm not married. But call me Florrie, if you like."

"Flossy, did you say?"

"No, Florrie." (She hadn't noticed before that the old woman was hard of hearing; but perhaps it was because she was across the room from her now instead of standing right beside her.)

"Florrie's a pretty name. Mine's Blanche, but nobody's called me that for years. Where do you work, Florrie?"

"At the university."

"The university . . . University Hospital, you mean?"

"No. I'm in the Arts Building. I teach."

"You teach art?"

"No, I teach Canadian history."

"Oh, so you're a teacher. I wanted to teach when I was a girl. I wanted to teach so bad. But my mother wouldn't let me. She made me take a dressmaking course instead."

"And did that work out? Did you enjoy dressmaking?"

"Oh, well enough. But that wasn't the way I earned a living when I had to. I kept a boardinghouse. For years. And do you know where I kept a boardinghouse?"

"Some other town? Here in Saskatoon?"

"Right here where we're standing. My boardinghouse was where this building is now."

"Oh. Then you must've made some money when this building was built."

"Well, yes, you could say so. But I was sorry to see my house torn down. Oh, my goodness, I was sorry. All those years and all those people."

"That must've been quite an experience, eh? Lots of people coming and going. Did you have a family too?"

"Two sons. Perce, my second son, works for the Post Office. If you're ever around at noon, you may see him coming and going in the hall. He has his lunch with me three days a week. Perce and his wife brought up his family in that house of mine; but when it was sold my daughter-in-law wanted their own house separate." (There was resentment in her voice. A sore point, Florrie conjectured.)

"You have grandchildren, then?" Florrie asked politely. Older people always like to talk about their grandchildren.

"Oh, yes. Three boys and a girl. One of the boys is going to university too. In Regina. He's very clever. He's so clever I can't understand a word he says sometimes."

She was still talking happily about the grandchildren some time later when Florrie decided she must leave.

"Oh, no, Mrs. Cornish, not another cup of tea. I must get back to my marking. Must hand back their essays tomorrow, you know."

"Oh, you teachers. You always work so hard. Won't you take some of the lemon bread with you? Or some of this nut bread?"

"No, no—really, Mrs. Cornish, you mustn't stuff me. Save it for your son's lunch. I must be off."

A sweet old soul, she thought, back at her own dining table, over which the essays were scattered. A sweet old soul, but almost too chatty.

3

The old woman was restless. The tall apartment building seemed to her almost creepily quiet. The builders had boasted, justifiably, of the soundproofing between apartments, so that, even if her hearing had been good, she could not have heard her neighbours unless they had given the loudest and noisiest of parties. And they were all so quiet. Most of them were widows, like herself, or retired people. No life left in them. She used to knock at Mrs. Baron's door farther down the hall, hoping for a little gab, but lately Mrs. Baron didn't answer the door. She must either be sleeping or too deaf to hear her. And of course that school teacher—Flossy, had she said her name was?—was out all day. But now she was in. The old woman could see the light shining under the door.

When she knocked at the door, Flossy—no, Florrie it was—came to answer, the tap still turned on at the kitchen sink. "Oh, Mrs. Cornish," she said, "I thought you were the paper boy. I'm just getting myself some dinner."

"Why don't you come and have a bite with me? I've got enough for two," Mrs. Cornish said eagerly.

"Oh, I couldn't. I've already put things on. I'm afraid I don't have enough for two, but why don't you come and have some coffee with me—say nine or nine thirty?"

The old woman was back at eight. "I forgot what time you said," she told Florrie.

"Oh well, never mind. I'll put the coffee on to perk, and you can have some ice cream with me while we wait for it to be ready."

She pushed aside a pile of books at the end of the dining table, dished up the ice cream in heavy cereal bowls, with fruit poured over it.

"How are you finding the children?" the old woman asked.

"The children?"

"The children you teach. You did say you were a teacher?"

"Oh, they're not children—at least they don't think they are. I'm at the university. Remember?"

Mrs. Cornish fumbled with the brooch—her mother's amethyst brooch—which fastened her collar. It was something she did when she was embarrassed. She was always forgetting things, or not hearing things clearly. Was this woman a student? Come to think of it, she looked younger than she had thought at first, with her hair falling around her face. She peered at Florrie with her dim old eyes; then her gaze wandered to a painting on the wall above the dining table. It was an odd painting, rather sad, with dark, diminished human figures clinging together on a park bench under brown trees. "Did you paint that?" she asked Florrie.

"Oh, no, I'm no artist. My uncle's a painter. He did that. Do you like it?"

"Very much," Mrs. Cornish lied, "but isn't it just a little—gloomy?"

"Oh, Uncle George's work is gloomy. He got his start as a war-time painter with the Canadian Armed Services. He painted all those great, dark canvasses, with khaki uniforms and gray skies and mud. All brown and gray, with a hint of blood-red now and then. He's never got away from his war-time style in peace-time subjects. At least he uses the same colors."

"But he came back from the War. He wasn't killed, like Matt, my son."

"You had a son killed?"

The coffee was ready, and Florrie poured it into two big brown mugs. The old woman found her mug heavy to hold. She had broken her wrist two years ago when she fell on the ice, and it was still weak.

Matt's face, with his naval cap at a jaunty angle, as in his last photograph, hovered just in front of Mrs. Cornish's eyes, cut off her vision. "It was a submarine got him," she said. "Those Germans."

"I hardly remember the War," Florrie said, almost apologetically. "I was just a small child then. It must've been terrible for you."

"I'll never forget the day I found out," Mrs. Cornish went on. "Never. I'll never get over it. You know, I've never been to church since."

"You found you couldn't believe?" Flossy—Florrie?—asked. "Because God allowed your son's death?"

Mrs. Cornish considered this. What had belief to do with it? "It was because he always went to church. He was such a good boy. I couldn't go to church without being reminded of him. Ida—my daughter-in-law—keeps trying to get me to go. She says it would be consoling. But I'll never go. Never."

For a moment she had almost thought Florrie was Ida, and she must argue with her.

"Still, you have your other son," Florrie said. "You have your grandchildren."

So she was supposed to be lucky, the old woman thought. Count her blessings.

"Tell me about the days when you ran the boardinghouse," Florrie said. "Are some of the people who boarded with you still around?"

So she wanted to change the subject, did she? Take her mind off Matt? Perhaps just as well.

"Most of them are dead or moved," Mrs. Cornish said. "Some of them are too high up now to want to remember when they lived in a boardinghouse. Some of them are old, too. But some of them come back. Only last year a couple came back . . ."

What were their names? They had become engaged at her place, those two. She frowned, laboriously trying to remember. Then faces, incidents, began to come back. She talked on, began to realize that she had been here at Florrie's a long time, saw Florrie stealing a glance at her wrist watch. Mustn't wear out her welcome. She lumbered to her feet, and Florrie rose to help her.

"Don't mark the children's papers too hard," she told Florrie.

4

Florrie was full of anxiety about this job, which she felt she must do well on. She had been late getting her doctorate, and full-time permanent academic jobs were becoming scarce. She was lucky to be here, and she must make a good impression, earn tenure and promotion. She was conscientious about her teaching and although she didn't think of herself as drivingly ambitious, she was ambitious enough. She didn't have too much time for distractions, especially distractions she didn't enjoy. When the old woman took to knocking on her door every evening, she became just such a distraction.

"You were late coming in tonight," the old woman said one evening.

"How do you know?" Florrie asked. "Do you watch when I come in?"

"I walked past several times earlier, and your lights weren't on. Now they're on. I could see the light shining under the door."

So that was it.

Late the next afternoon, Florrie came in quietly, did not turn on the light in the hall, but reached around the corner to turn on the kitchen light. That, she was more or less certain, did not show outside in the hall.

That evening, she heard the old woman limping several times along the hall. Once she halted in front of Florrie's door, but she did not knock. Florrie held her breath, pen poised over paper. Then she heard the old woman's slow, halting walk along the passageway towards her own door. Florrie felt guilty, as though she had hidden from her grandmother. But she couldn't, she just couldn't, chat with the old dear, sweet as she was, for hours every evening. If she would come just once a week, say Sunday afternoon—or every other Sunday afternoon—

But then, Sunday was the day Perce and Ida came and took the old woman out to Sunday dinner. Florrie knew, because she had met them once in the hall, on the way out. She had been wrapped up in her dressing gown, on the way to put some clothes in the washer; she would have liked to ignore them, and be ignored, but the old woman had stopped her, had insisted on introducing her, though as usual she couldn't remember Florrie's name. Perce was a mild little man, Ida the dominant one in that family, Florrie conjectured.

Florrie almost never turned her light on in the hall now. After all, she told herself, she might as well save power. It was some time before she talked again to the old woman; but one Saturday afternoon in late November, coming in with a load of groceries, she

found herself sharing the elevator with her. "Oh, it's Flossy—
Flossy Milton, isn't it?" the old woman beamed. "What have you
been doing with yourself?"

"Oh, I've been here. Busy."

"You've been on the night shift at the hospital, haven't you? I
never see your light any longer."

Florrie felt guilty immediately, and invited the old woman to
come in to tea. Thank goodness she had bought cake at the bakery;
otherwise the poor old soul would probably have wanted to cook
something for her. She looked at Mrs. Cornish, perched rather
forlornly on the chesterfield in the living room. Was it her imagination, or had the old woman gone downhill, even in these few
months?

One evening, when Florrie was sitting up late marking December
examinations, her doorbell—the one down on the main floor—
rang. Who could be ringing her doorbell at midnight? Was it a
prank or an emergency? She crossed the room, pressed a button,
and spoke into the intercom. "Yes. Who is it?"

"It's me," a woman's voice said, rather loudly.

"Who's me? I think you must have the wrong place. I wasn't
expecting anybody."

She went back to her work, but the bell rang again immediately.

"Who's this?" she asked in exasperated tones.

The voice was desperate. "Me, Me, Me. Let me in."

"Can't you tell your name? I can't let in someone I don't
know."

"It's—it's—Cornish. I've locked myself out of my apartment
and I can't get the caretaker."

"Oh—well, of course, come on up." She pressed the button that
opened the front door, stepped out in the hall to see the old woman
when she got off the elevator.

"You must say your name, Mrs. Cornish," she said. "Voices
sound different over the intercom, you know."

"I forgot it for a minute," the old woman said, woebegone. "The
caretaker usually lets me in. He must be out."

"Maybe he was in bed," Florrie said. "It's getting late. Where
were you? At your son's?"

"No, I was just out walking."

By herself? At midnight? Oh dear. The poor woman.

Florrie telephoned the caretaker. His doorbell, he said, hadn't rung, but he'd come and let Mrs. Cornish in. She usually left her keys on the kitchen table, he said.

Florrie met the son in the hall by chance a few days later. "You must have quite a problem sometimes with Mother," he said, shaking his head. "I can imagine."

Florrie smiled uncomfortably. "Of course, she's a dear . . ." she said. Ought she, she wondered, to suggest that Perce and Ida take Mrs. Cornish home to live with them? But they saw her regularly; they must know how she was. Probably Ida wouldn't have her, in any case.

The morning she took the taxi to the airport to fly to Winnipeg for the Christmas holiday, she stopped on the way to the elevator to prop a parcel up against Mrs. Cornish's door. Gift of guilt, she thought, half smiling. Chocolates to make up for her neglect. But if she had thought she would get away without a few words with the old woman, she was mistaken. Florrie had reached the elevator and was pressing the button when Mrs. Cornish's door opened suddenly and she peered out. She picked up the parcel, waved at Florrie, and came hobbling towards her. "Somebody must've left a parcel at my door by mistake," she said.

"It's yours," Florrie said, repeating the words twice because the old woman couldn't hear. "Your name's on it. It's a parcel from me."

"Isn't she a darling?" the old woman said to the caretaker"s wife, who was passing through the hall. "She's given me a present."

The elevator came. "Can't stay—taxi's waiting—Merry Christmas!" Florrie called back, shutting her eyes as the elevator plunged with her down to ground level. Ah, how good to have a little time away from students, faculty, committee meetings—and from Mrs. Cornish!

5

Sometimes when the old woman awoke in the morning she was not the old woman or Mrs. Cornish. She was Blanche, little Blanche Tissington on her way to school with her lunch in a red lard-kettle;

or young Blanche Tissington going to a dance all dolled up in her best. Oh, she was a lively one, that Blanche Tissington, with her dimples and her curls and her twinkling eyes and feet. Flossy Milton (or whatever her name was) would never guess. And it was hard, if you had been little Blanche Tissington when you woke up in the morning, to find yourself imprisoned in old Mrs. Cornish's body, which was so heavy and stiff. What a to-do it was just to take a bath, to let yourself down gradually, your knee-joints creaking, into the tub; and then to hoist yourself up and out when the bath was over. And it was either that or take a shower, which was even more dangerous. Remember the old man in the boardinghouse who had slipped, who had broken his hip, who had nearly drowned.

It was hard, now, to keep times and seasons separate. She had to look out the window to see if the snow was still on the ground or if the trees were coming out into new leaves. In the morning she was not sure of the time because she had forgotten to wind the kitchen clock and it had stopped. Her watch never had been reliable. The radio told her the time of day, and the newspaper told her the date, but she forgot what they told her from one hour to the next.

It was lilac season when she met that Flossy person in the hall, and she—Flossy? Florrie?—said, "Why don't you come to dinner tonight?"

"Oh, you're always so busy," the old woman said.

"Not tonight. It's vacation. I'm going away soon for the summer."

So she went to Florrie's for dinner; and Florrie had roasted a chicken and cooked a pie. She wouldn't have thought Florrie was so domestic.

"Somebody knocked at my door asking for a relative of yours," the old woman said. "At least, he asked for Dr. Middleton. I told him there was a nurse named Middleton here, but no doctor that I knew of."

"I'm Dr. Middleton," Florrie said.

"You are! You never told me you were a doctor. I thought you were a nurse."

"I'm not a nurse. It's just my doctorate of Philosophy. Who was he? The man who asked for me?"

The old woman didn't understand all that, but she tried to remember the man. "He didn't tell me his name," she said. "He

was tall. I think he was fair—or was he dark? He had a moustache,
I think."

"Are you sure it wasn't a beard?"

Florrie was laughing at her. Oh—wait until she was old, really
old. Then she would know.

In the fall—it must have been fall, because the leaves were changing
color—one day when she was on her way out of the apartment
building, she saw Florrie in the lobby with a man. The same man?
He had a moustache, not a beard. He reminded her in some distant
way, she realized, of Edward Cornish, her husband, who had gone
away such a long time ago. But she never mentioned Edward
Cornish, never. It was only her son she missed. Matt. Put the
thought of Edward out of her mind. He was not to be remembered.
Even after all these years. She scuttled past Florrie and the man and
out the door without speaking. Now why did she do that? What
would Florrie think? She clutched her brooch and sighed.

Not long afterwards, Florrie moved out of her apartment, although
not out of the building. "I'm just moving up to the sixteenth floor,
Mrs. Cornish," she told the old woman. "I'll still be a neighbor."

"But I'll never remember where it is," the old woman said.
Then, "Why do you want to move?"

"I need more space. For a study. This apartment is really very
small, you know."

The old woman looked around the living room. "It's as big as
mine," she said forlornly. But of course if she wanted to go—

One day when she had started to walk home from shopping, the
old woman stopped to rest on a bench in front of the Public
Library. She was just closing her eyes for a little snooze when she
heard a voice. "Why, Mrs. Cornish," the voice said, "what are you
doing here? Are you all right?"

It was Florrie.

"I'm just resting," the old woman said. "I was wondering if I'd
make it the rest of the way home."

"Would you like to take my arm? I can help you."

So the old woman got up, and allowed Florrie to lead her. She
hoped she was not delaying her too much; she had to take such tiny
steps.

"Would you like to see my new apartment?" Florrie asked when they arrived in the lobby. "Come up and I'll make you some tea and toast."

So she went up; and really it was a much bigger, more elaborate apartment altogether. But there was Florrie's dining table with the books on it, and there was her funny, gloomy painting by the man who had been in the War. (Oh, Matt, Matt, where are you?)

"You see I have a really fine view across the river," Florrie said. "I sit here at breakfast and watch the traffic on the bridge."

Yes. That was more cheerful than the painting.

But there was someone at the door. It was that man, the man with the moustache, though he no longer had the moustache. Or was it a different man? He didn't look like Edward Cornish after all. It must have been the way the light had fallen on him.

"Oh, Reg," Florrie said. She sounded as though she were used to him. Then, "Mrs. Cornish, I think you met Reg once in the hall, didn't you?"

"You're the lady who thought Florrie was a nurse," he said, smiling at the old woman. "Lucky you never tested her with a sprained ankle."

"We're having toast and honey, Reg," Florrie said. "Do you want some too?"

"There's nothing I'd like more than toast and honey. Almost nothing."

He was a pleasant man, and she could see he was prepared to be kind to old ladies. But it was not the same. No, it was not the same. She did not stay long.

But she had to go back. She had to go back and knock at Florrie's door again, because she couldn't find her own apartment. She had walked across the hall to it, and it wasn't there. Somebody else lived there.

She was almost crying when Florrie opened the door. "It's gone," she said. "My apartment's gone."

"Your apartment's gone?" Florrie said, staring at her. "It can't be."

Mrs. Cornish pointed across the hall. "Somebody named Jones lives there now. They must just have moved in."

"Oh!" Florrie exclaimed, as though something suddenly made sense. "You live on the fifth floor, Mrs. Cornish. don't you remember?"

"But isn't this the fifth floor?"

"No. The sixteenth. Just a minute and I'll come downstairs with you. Reg, I'll be right back, darling."

Oh, now she knew what she had done. She had been so foolish. Florrie and that man—Herbert, Reg—would laugh and laugh at her when they were alone together. She tugged at her brooch, clutched her handbag, felt herself go scarlet. Yes, she had her key. And here they were on the fifth floor, and at her door. Someone else, a young couple, lived in Florrie's apartment. She had never got acquainted with them.

6

Florrie dabbed at her eyes with a handkerchief. She wasn't sure whether she was sad or hysterically amused. Both, perhaps. "But what am I to do about her, Reg? She can't go wandering about the building not knowing where she lives."

"Do? But she has a son, doesn't she? You said she had a son. Isn't it up to him? Why should you do anything?"

"Well, I'll call him. I'll tell him about this. I wonder if he's home from the Post Office. I'd hate to get that awful wife of his."

Florrie detested telephoning. It was one of her little phobias. She would almost rather drop into the Post Office and look Perce up. But Perce mightn't like to be looked up. She picked up the phone book.

"I thought there wouldn't be many Cornishes," she said, "but there's a P. Cornish, a P.A. Cornish, a P.E. Cornish, an R.P. Cornish. I suppose Mrs. B. Cornish is our Mrs. Cornish."

"It sounds confusing. Why don't you write a letter to Mr. Percy Cornish at the Post Office?"

"I'm not sure if he's Percy or Percival. Well, yes, I think I'll write a letter, after all. It's easier that way. But ought I to? They'll put her in a nursing home, that's what they'll do. Would I want that done to me?"

"She isn't you, you know, Florrie."

"Isn't she? I'm not sure about that." She sighed.

But she would write the letter, just the same.

Florrie saw the old woman only one more time; sitting, as she had before, on a park bench, but this time in front of the cenotaph, with the last of the leaves falling around her. She was wearing a hat with a large brim, and her shopping basket was on the bench beside her. Her eyes were closed tight. This time Florrie did not disturb her. She walked by quietly and went home to the apartment. She would marry Reg, she decided. They would buy a house with a garden on the other side of the river, have puppies, kittens. Distractions, but she would enjoy them. Was there still time for a child? Not if she was sensible.

On her way upstairs, she stopped off on the fifth floor. Someone new had already moved into Mrs. Cornish's apartment. Had Perce and Ida taken her to live with them? Probably not. After all, would she?

Oh, she was already old, old. If she looked in her mirror, she was sure she would see Mrs. Cornish's face.

Responding

1. How does Florrie feel when Mrs. Cornish first starts visiting? How do her feelings toward the old woman change as the story unfolds? What causes the change?

2. In each section of the story, the author reveals Mrs. Cornish's decreasing ability to look after herself. Review the story's six parts and summarize what each reveals. In your view, is Mrs. Cornish in need of supervised care? Why or why not?

3. What conflict does Florrie experience in the final part of the story? What has Mrs. Cornish's fate made Florrie realize?

4. What does the story gain by being written from alternating points of view? Could the story have been told entirely through Florrie's eyes? Explain.

5. For a story to be effective, every detail should add to its development. Explain what the following details add to the meaning of this story:
   a) the excess of furniture in Mrs. Cornish's apartment.

b) the fact that Mrs. Cornish once ran a boarding house where the highrise now stands.

c) Mrs. Cornish's habit of fumbling with her mother's amethyst brooch.

d) the painting by Florrie's uncle.

e) Mrs. Cornish's sitting at the cenotaph in autumn.

6. Was Mrs. Cornish well looked after by her family and Florrie? Comment. What are some things that could be done to help people you know experience a dignified, happy old age?

7. Rewrite the story's ending by having Florrie talk to Mrs. Cornish at the cenotaph. What would each say to the other? How would the conversation end?

Student notes, page 249

7 STORIES FOR FURTHER READING

Each of us has already read and listened to numerous stories that focussed on a wide range of characters, conflicts, settings, and themes. We have had experiences with adventure stories, romance stories, detective, horror, and science fiction stories. This background helps us choose what we want to read next, and assists us in appreciating the meaning and significance of new stories.

The stories that follow offer readers further experiences with a wide variety of writing techniques and story types. "The Interlopers" shows us that life sometimes twists events ironically; "Penny in the Dust" illustrates how a simple object may become deeply meaningful; and "Flight" helps us to understand growth and freedom by parallelling the situation of a young woman with that of her grandfather's pigeons. "Barney" takes us to a remote island for the results of a bizarre experiment; "The Crooked Man" invites us to pit our observational skills against those of Sherlock Holmes in a traditional detective story; and "A Way Out of the Forest" arouses our sympathy for two children in a difficult predicament.

Saki (H. H. Munro)

THE INTERLOPERS

For three generations, their families have quarrelled. And now, armed with
rifles, Georg and Ulrich both vow to put an end to the long-standing feud.

I n a forest of mixed growth somewhere on the eastern spurs of
the Carpathians, a man stood one winter night watching and
listening, as though he waited for some beast of the woods to come
within the range of his vision, and, later, of his rifle. But the game
for whose presence he kept so keen an outlook was none that
figured in the sportsman's calendar as lawful and proper for the
chase; Ulrich von Gradwitz patrolled the dark forest in quest of a
human enemy.

The forest lands of Gradwitz were of wide extent and well
stocked with game; the narrow strip of precipitous woodland that
lay on its outskirt was not remarkable for the game it harbored or
the shooting it afforded, but it was the most jealously guarded of all
its owner's territorial possessions. A famous lawsuit, in the days of
his grandfather, had wrested it from the illegal possession of a
neighboring family of petty landowners; the dispossessed party had
never acquiesced in the judgment of the Courts, and a long series of
poaching affrays and similar scandals had embittered the relationships between the families for three generations. The neighbor feud
had grown into a personal one since Ulrich had come to be head of
his family; if there was a man in the world whom he detested and
wished ill to it was Georg Znaeym, the inheritor of the quarrel and

the tireless game-snatcher and raider of the disputed border-forest. The feud might, perhaps, have died down or been compromised if the personal ill will of the two men had not stood in the way. As boys they had thirsted for one another's blood, as men each prayed that misfortune might fall on the other. On this wind-scourged winter night Ulrich had banded together his foresters to watch the dark forest, not in quest of four-footed quarry, but to keep a look-out for the prowling thieves whom he suspected of being afoot from across the land boundary. The roebuck, which usually kept in the sheltered hollows during a storm-wind, were running like driven things tonight, and there was movement and unrest among the creatures that were wont to sleep through the dark hours. Assuredly there was a disturbing element in the forest, and Ulrich could guess the quarter from whence it came.

He strayed away by himself from the watchers whom he had placed in ambush on the crest of the hill, and wandered far down the steep slopes amid the wild tangle of undergrowth, peering through the tree-trunks and listening through the whistling and skirling of the wind and the restless beating of the branches for sight or sound of the marauders. If only on this wild night, in this dark, lone spot, he might come across Georg Znaeym, man to man, with none to witness—that was the wish that was uppermost in his thoughts. And as he stepped round the trunk of a huge beech he came face to face with the man he sought.

The two enemies stood glaring at one another for a long silent moment. Each had a rifle in his hand, each had hate in his heart and murder uppermost in his mind. The chance had come to give full play to the passions of a lifetime. But a man who has been brought up under the code of a restraining civilization cannot easily nerve himself to shoot down his neighbor in cold blood and without word spoken, except for an offence against his hearth and honor. And before the moment of hesitation had given way to action a deed of Nature's own violence overwhelmed them both. A fierce shriek of the storm had been answered by a splitting crash over their heads, and ere they could leap aside a mass of falling beech tree had thundered down on them. Ulrich von Gradwitz found himself stretched on the ground, one arm numb beneath him and the other held almost as helplessly in a tight tangle of forked branches, while both legs were pinned beneath the fallen mass. His heavy shooting-boots had saved his feet from being crushed to pieces, but if his fractures were not as serious as they might have been, at least it was evident that he could not move from his present position till someone came to release him. The descending twigs had slashed the skin of his face, and he had to wink away some drops of blood from his eyelashes before he could take in a general view of the disaster. At his side, so near that under ordinary circumstances he could almost have touched him, lay Georg Znaeym, alive and struggling, but obviously as helplessly pinioned down as himself. All round them lay a thick-strewn wreckage of splintered branches and broken twigs.

Relief at being alive and exasperation at his captive plight brought a strange medley of pious thank-offerings and sharp curses to Ulrich's lips. Georg, who was nearly blinded with the blood which trickled across his eyes, stopped his struggling for a moment to listen, and then gave a short, snarling laugh.

"So you're not killed, as you ought to be, but you're caught, anyway," he cried; "caught fast. Ho, what a jest, Ulrich von Gradwitz snared in his stolen forest. There's real justice for you!"

And he laughed again, mockingly and savagely.

"I'm caught in my own forest-land," retorted Ulrich. "When my men come to release us you will wish, perhaps, that you were in a better plight than caught poaching on a neighbor's land, shame on you."

Georg was silent for a moment; then he answered quietly:

"Are you sure that your men will find much to release? I have men, too, in the forest tonight, close behind me, and *they* will be here first and do the releasing. When they drag me out from under these damned branches it won't need much clumsiness on their part to roll this mass of trunk right over on the top of you. Your men will find you dead under a fallen beech tree. For form's sake I shall send my condolences to your family."

"It is a useful hint," said Ulrich fiercely. "My men had orders to follow in ten minutes' time, seven of which must have gone by already, and when they get me out—I will remember the hint. Only as you will have met your death poaching on my lands, I don't think I can decently send any message of condolence to your family."

"Good," snarled Georg, "good. We fight this quarrel out to the death, you and I and our foresters, with no cursed interlopers to come between us. Death and damnation to you, Ulrich von Gradwitz."

"The same to you, Georg Znaeym, forest-thief, game-snatcher."

Both men spoke with the bitterness of possible defeat before them, for each knew that it might be long before his men would seek him out or find him; it was a bare matter of chance which party would arrive first on the scene.

Both had now given up the useless struggle to free themselves from the mass of wood that held them down. Ulrich limited his endeavors to an effort to bring his one partially free arm near enough to his outer coat-pocket to draw out his wine-flask. Even when he had accomplished that operation it was long before he could manage the unscrewing of the stopper or get any of the liquid down his throat. But what a Heaven-sent draught it seemed! It was an open winter, and little snow had fallen as yet, hence the captives suffered less from the cold than might have been the case at that season of the year; nevertheless, the wine was warming and reviving to the wounded man, and he looked across with something like a throb of pity to where his enemy lay, just keeping the groans of pain and weariness from crossing his lips.

"Could you reach this flask if I threw it over to you?" asked Ulrich suddenly; "there is good wine in it, and one may as well be as comfortable as one can. Let us drink, even if tonight one of us dies."

"No, I can scarcely see anything; there is so much blood caked round my eyes," said Georg, "and in any case I don't drink wine with an enemy."

Ulrich was silent for a few minutes, and lay listening to the weary screeching of the wind. An idea was slowly forming and growing in his brain, an idea that gained strength every time that he looked across at the man who was fighting so grimly against pain and exhaustion. In the pain and languor that Ulrich himself was feeling the old fierce hatred seemed to be dying down.

"Neighbor," he said presently, "do as you please if your men come first. It was a fair compact. But as for me, I've changed my mind. If my men are the first to come you shall be the first to be helped, as though you were my guest. We have quarrelled like devils all our lives over this stupid strip of forest, where the trees can't even stand upright in a breath of wind. Lying here tonight, thinking, I've come to think we've been rather fools; there are better things in life than getting the better of a boundary dispute. Neighbor, if you will help me to bury the old quarrel I—I will ask you to be my friend."

Georg Znaeym was silent for so long that Ulrich thought, perhaps, he had fainted with the pain of his injuries. Then he spoke slowly and in jerks.

"How the whole region would stare and gabble if we rode into the market-square together. No one living can remember seeing a Znaeym and a Von Gradwitz talking to one another in friendship. And what peace there would be among the forester folk if we ended our feud tonight. And if we choose to make peace among our people there is none other to interfere, no interlopers from outside.——You would come and keep the Sylvester night beneath my roof, and I would come and feast on some high day at your castle.——I would never fire a shot on your land, save when you invited me as a guest; and you should come and shoot with me down in the marshes where the wildfowl are. In all the countryside there are none that could hinder if we willed to make peace. I never thought to have wanted to do other than hate you all my life, but I think I have changed my mind about things too, this last half-hour. And you offered me your wineflask.——Ulrich von Gradwitz, I will be your friend."

For a space both men were silent, turning over in their minds the wonderful changes that this dramatic reconcilation would bring about. In the cold, gloomy forest, with the wind tearing in fitful gusts through the naked branches and whistling round the tree-trunks, they lay and waited for the help that would now bring release and succor to both parties. And each prayed a private prayer that his men might be the first to arrive, so that he might be the first to show honorable attention to the enemy that had become a friend.

Presently, as the wind dropped for a moment, Ulrich broke silence.

"Let's shout for help," he said; "in this lull our voices may carry a little way."

"They won't carry far through the trees and undergrowth," said Georg, "but we can try. Together, then."

The two raised their voices in a prolonged hunting call.

"Together again," said Ulrich a few minutes later, after listening in vain for an answering halloo.

"I heard something that time, I think," said Ulrich.

"I heard nothing but the pestilential wind," said Georg hoarsely.

There was silence again for some minutes, and then Ulrich gave a joyful cry.

"I can see figures coming through the wood. They are following in the way I came down the hillside."

Both men raised their voices in as loud a shout as they could muster.

"They hear us! They've stopped. Now they see us. They're running down the hill towards us," cried Ulrich.

"How many of them are there?" asked Georg.

"I can't see distinctly," said Ulrich; "nine or ten."

"Then they are yours," said Georg; "I had only seven out with me."

"They are making all the speed they can, brave lads," said Ulrich gladly.

"Are they your men?" asked Georg. "Are they your men?" he repeated impatiently as Ulrich did not answer.

"No," said Ulrich with a laugh, the idiotic chattering laugh of a man unstrung with hideous fear.

"Who are they?" asked Georg quickly, straining his eyes to see what the other would gladly not have seen.

"*Wolves.*"

Responding

1. Where does this story take place? How do you know?

2. Using information provided in the first two paragraphs, discuss the influence of the past and tradition on a) the plot, b) the conflict, and on c) Ulrich and Georg's motivation.

3. What causes the change in attitude in the two enemies?

4. What is the surprise ending? Do you think the story's ending and title are appropriate? Why or why not?

5. Find one example in this story of each of the three types of irony mentioned in the Glossary. Share them with the class.

6. Tell about a feud or quarrel you, your family, or someone you know once had with someone else. What caused the feud? Was it ever resolved? If so, how? If not, why not?

Student notes, page 250

Ernest Buckler

PENNY IN
THE DUST

*Memories of those we love . . . some painful, others to be treasured—like a
shiny new penny.*

My sister and I were walking through the old sun-still fields
the evening before my father's funeral, recalling this memory or that—trying, after the fashion of families who gather again in
the place where they were born, to identify ourselves with the
strange children we must have been.

"Do you remember the afternoon we thought you were lost?"
my sister said. I did. That was as long ago as the day I was seven,
but I'd had occasion to remember it only yesterday.

"We searched everywhere," she said. "Up in the meeting-house,
back in the blueberry barrens—we even looked in the well. I think
it's the only time I ever saw Father really upset. He didn't even stop
to take the oxen off the wagon tongue when they told him. He raced
right through the chopping where Tom Reeve was burning brush,
looking for you—right through the flames almost; they couldn't do
a thing with him. And you up in your bed, sound asleep!"

"It was all over losing a penny or something, wasn't it?" she went
on, when I didn't answer. It was. She laughed indulgently. "You
were a crazy kid, weren't you."

I was. But there was more to it than that. I had never seen a
shining new penny before that day. I'd thought they were all black.
This one was bright as gold. And my father had given it to me.

You would have to understand about my father, and that is the
hard thing to tell. If I say that he worked all day long but never once

197

had I seen him hurry, that would make him sound like a stupid man. If I say that he never held me on his knee when I was a child and that I never heard him laugh out loud in his life, it would make him sound humorless and severe. If I said that whenever I'd be reeling off some of my fanciful plans and he'd come into the kitchen and I'd stop short, you'd think that he was distant and that in some kind of way I was afraid of him. None of that would be true.

There's no way you can tell it to make it sound like anything more than an inarticulate man a little at sea with an imaginative child. You'll have to take my word for it that there was more to it than that. It was as if his sure-footed way in the fields forsook him the moment he came near the door of my child's world and that he could never intrude on it without feeling awkward and conscious of trespass; and that I, sensing that but not understanding it, felt at the sound of his solid step outside, the child-world's foolish fragility. He would fix the small spot where I planted beans and other quick-sprouting seeds before he prepared the big garden, even if the spring was late; but he wouldn't ask me how many rows I wanted and if he made three rows and I wanted four, I couldn't ask him to change them. If I walked behind the load of hay, longing to ride, and he walked ahead of the oxen, I couldn't ask him to put me up and he wouldn't make any move to do so until he saw me trying to grasp the binder.

He, my father, had just given me a new penny, bright as gold.

He'd taken it from his pocket several times, pretending to examine the date on it, waiting for me to notice it. He couldn't offer me *anything* until I had shown some sign that the gift would be welcome.

"You can have it if you want it, Pete," he said at last.

"Oh, thanks," I said. Nothing more. I couldn't expose any of my eagerness either.

I started with it, to the store. For a penny you could buy the magic cylinder of "Long Tom" popcorn with Heaven knows what glittering bauble inside. But the more I thought of my bright penny disappearing forever into the black drawstring pouch the store-keeper kept his money in, the slower my steps lagged as the store came nearer and nearer. I sat down in the road.

It was that time of magic suspension in an August afternoon. The lifting smells of leaves and cut clover hung still in the sun. The sun drowsed, like a kitten curled up on my shoulder. The deep flour-fine dust in the road puffed about my bare ankles, warm and soft as sleep. The sound of the cowbells came sharp and hollow from the cool swamp.

I began to play with the penny, putting off the decision. I would close my eyes and bury it deep in the sand; and then, with my eyes still closed, get up and walk around, and then come back to search for it. Tantalizing myself, each time, with the excitement of discovering afresh its bright shining edge. I did that again and again. Alas, once too often.

It was almost dark when their excited talking in the room awakened me. It was Mother who had found me. I suppose when it came dusk she thought of me in my bed other nights, and I suppose she looked there without any reasonable hope but only as you look in every place where the thing that is lost has ever lain before. And now suddenly she was crying because when she opened the door there, miraculously, I was.

"Peter!" she cried, ignoring the obvious in her sudden relief, "*where* have you been?"

"I lost my penny," I said.

"You lost your penny . . .? But what made you come up here and hide?"

If Father hadn't been there, I might have told her the whole story. But when I looked up at Father, standing there like the shape of everything sound and straight, it was like daylight shredding the memory of a silly dream. How could I bear the shame of repeating before him the childish visions I had built in my head in the magic August afternoon when almost anything could be made to seem real, as I buried the penny and dug it up again? How could I explain that pit-of-the-stomach sickness which struck through the whole day when I had to believe, at last, that it was really gone? How could I explain that I wasn't really hiding from *them*? How, with the words and the understanding I had then, that this was the only possible place to run from that awful feeling of loss?

"I lost my penny," I said again. I looked at Father and turned my face into the pillow. "I want to go to sleep."

"Peter," Mother said, "it's almost nine o'clock. You haven't had a bite of supper. Do you know you almost scared the *life* out of us?"

"You better get some supper," Father said. It was the only time he had spoken.

I never dreamed that he would mention the thing again. But the next morning when we had the hay forks in our hands, ready to toss out the clover, he seemed to postpone the moment of actually leaving for the field. He stuck his fork in the ground and brought in another pail of water, though the kettle was chock full. He took out the shingle nail that held a broken yoke strap together and put it back in exactly the same hole. He went into the shed to see if the pigs had cleaned up all their breakfast.

And then he said abruptly: "Ain't you got no idea where you lost your penny?"

"Yes," I said, "I know just about."

"Let's see if we can't find it," he said.

We walked down the road together, stiff with awareness. He didn't hold my hand.

"It's right here somewhere," I said. "I was playin' with it, in the dust."

He looked at me, but he didn't ask me what game anyone could possibly play with a penny in the dust.

I might have known he would find it. He could tap the alder bark with his jack-knife just exactly hard enough so it wouldn't split but so it would twist free from the notched wood, to make a whistle. His great fingers could trace loose the hopeless snarl of a fishing line that I could only succeed in tangling tighter and tighter. If I broke the handle of my wheelbarrow ragged beyond sight of any possible repair, he could take it and bring it back to me so you could hardly see the splice if you weren't looking for it.

He got down on his knees and drew his fingers carefully through the dust, like a harrow; not clawing it frantically into heaps as I had done, covering even as I uncovered. He found the penny almost at once.

He held it in his hand, as if the moment of passing it to me were a deadline for something he dreaded to say, but must. Something that could not be put off any longer, if it were to spoken at all.

"Pete," he said, "you needn'ta hid. I wouldn'ta beat you."

"*Beat* me? Oh, Father! You didn't think that was the reason ...?" I felt almost sick. I felt as if I had struck *him*.

I had to tell him the truth then. Because only the truth, no matter how ridiculous it was, would have the unmistakable sound truth has, to scatter that awful idea out of his head.

"I wasn't hidin', Father," I said, "honest. I was . . . I was buryin' my penny and makin' out I was diggin' up treasure. I was makin' out I was findin' gold. I didn't know what to *do* when I lost it, I just didn't know where to *go* . . ." His head was bent forward, like mere listening. I had to make it truer still.

"I made out it was gold," I said desperately, "and I—I was makin' out I bought you a mowin' machine so's you could get your work done early every day so's you and I could go in to town in the big automobile I made out I bought you—and everyone'd turn around and look at us drivin' down the streets . . ." His head was perfectly still, as if he were only waiting with patience for me to finish. "*Laugh*in' and *talk*in'," I said. Louder, smiling intensely, com*pell*ing him, by the absolute conviction of some true particular, to believe me.

He looked up then. It was the only time I had ever seen tears in his eyes. It was the only time in my seven years that he had ever put his arm around me.

I wondered, though, why he hesitated, and then put the penny back in his own pocket.

Yesterday I knew. I never found any fortune and we never had a car to ride in together. But I think he knew what that would be like, just the same. I found the penny again yesterday, when we were getting out his good suit—in an upper vest pocket where no one ever carries change. It was still shining. He must have kept it polished.

I left it there.

Responding

1. What key information about plot and character is given in the story's first sentence?

2. The episodes of this narrative are not in chronological order. What is the purpose of the flashback?

3. a) What happens in the time between the paragraph, on page 199 (that ends "Alas, once too often.") and the beginning of the following paragraph ("It was almost dark . . .")?
   b) Why is that plot information not given directly?

4. What is the main misunderstanding centring around the lost penny?

5. Do you feel that the father did the right thing with the penny at the end of the story? Write your response in a paragraph. Share it with your group or the class.

6. The penny in this selection is symbolic. What does it represent to the father when he first gives it to his son? What does it represent to him later on? What does the penny represent to the son when he first receives it? What does it mean to him at the end of the story?

7. Write about a time in your childhood when you were embarrassed or misunderstood.

Student notes, page 250

Doris Lessing

FLIGHT

A stubborn old man attempts to hang on to a favorite bird and a favorite granddaughter. And, as he learns, letting go isn't easy for others either.

*A*bove the old man's head was the dovecote, a tall wire-netted shelf on stilts, full of strutting, preening birds. The sunlight broke on their gray breasts into small rainbows. His ears were lulled by their crooning, his hands stretched up towards his favorite, a homing pigeon, a young plump-bodied bird which stood still when it saw him and cocked a shrewd bright eye.

"Pretty, pretty, pretty," he said, as he grasped the bird and drew it down, feeling the cold coral claws tighten around his finger. Content, he rested the bird lightly on his chest, and leaned against a tree, gazing out beyond the dovecote into the landscape of a late afternoon. In folds and hollows of sunlight and shade, the dark red soil, which was broken into great dusty clods, stretched wide to a tall horizon. Trees marked the course of the valley; a stream of rich green grass the road.

His eyes travelled homewards along this road until he saw his granddaughter swinging on the gate underneath a frangipani tree. Her hair fell down her back in a wave of sunlight, and her long bare legs repeated the angles of the frangipani stems, bare, shining-brown stems among patterns of pale blossoms.

She was gazing past the pink flowers, past the railway cottage where they lived, along the road to the village.

His mood shifted. He deliberately held out his wrist for the bird to take flight, and caught it again at the moment it spread its wings. He felt the plump shape strive and strain under his fingers; and, in a sudden access of troubled spite, shut the bird into a small box and fastened the bolt. "Now you stay there," he muttered; and turned his back on the shelf of birds. He moved warily along the hedge, stalking his granddaughter, who was now looped over the gate, her head loose on her arms, singing. The light happy sound mingled with the crooning of the birds, and his anger mounted.

"Hey!" he shouted; saw her jump, look back, and abandon the gate. Her eyes veiled themselves, and she said in a pert neutral voice: "Hullo, Grandad." Politely she moved towards him, after a lingering backward glance at the road.

"Waiting for Steven, hey?" he said, his fingers curling like claws into his palm.

"Any objection?" she asked lightly, refusing to look at him.

He confronted her, his eyes narrowed, shoulders hunched, tight in a hard knot of pain which included the preening birds, the sunlight, the flowers. He said: "Think you're old enough to go courting, hey?"

The girl tossed her head at the old-fashioned phrase and sulked, "Oh, Grandad!"

"Think you want to leave home, hey? Think you can go running around the fields at night?"

Her smile made him see her, as he had every evening of this warm end-of-summer month, swinging hand in hand along the road to the village with that red-handed, red-throated, violent-bodied youth, the son of the postmaster. Misery went to his head and he shouted angrily: "I'll tell your mother!"

"Tell away!" she said, laughing, and went back to the gate.

He heard her singing, for him to hear:

> '*I've got you under my skin,*
> *I've got you deep in the heart of . . .*'

"Rubbish," he shouted. "Rubbish. Impudent little bit of rubbish!"

Growling under his breath he turned towards the dovecote, which was his refuge from the house he shared with his daughter and her husband and their children. But now the house would be empty. Gone all the young girls with their laughter and their squabbling and their teasing. He would be left, uncherished and alone, with that square-fronted, calm-eyed woman, his daughter.

He stooped, muttering, before the dovecote, resenting the absorbed cooing birds.

From the gate the girl shouted: "Go and tell! Go on, what are you waiting for?"

Obstinately he made his way to the house, with quick, pathetic persistent glances of appeal back at her. But she never looked around. Her defiant but anxious young body stung him into love and repentance. He stopped. "But I never meant . . ." he muttered, waiting for her to turn and run to him. "I didn't mean . . ."

She did not turn. She had forgotten him. Along the road came the young man Steven, with something in his hand. A present for her? The old man stiffened as he watched the gate swing back, and the couple embrace. In the brittle shadows of the frangipani tree his grand-daughter, his darling, lay in the arms of the postmaster's son, and her hair flowed back over his shoulder.

"I see you!" shouted the old man spitefully. They did not move. He stumped into the little whitewashed house, hearing the wooden veranda creak angrily under his feet. His daughter was sewing in the front room, threading a needle held to the light.

He stopped again, looking back into the garden. The couple were now sauntering among the bushes, laughing. As he watched he saw the girl escape from the youth with a sudden mischievous movement, and run off through the flowers with him in pursuit. He heard shouts, laughter, a scream, silence.

"But it's not like that at all," he muttered miserably. "It's not like that. Why can't you see? Running and giggling, and kissing and kissing. You'll come to something quite different."

He looked at his daughter with sardonic hatred, hating himself. They were caught and finished, both of them, but the girl was still running free.

"Can't you *see*?" he demanded of his invisible granddaughter, who was at that moment lying in the thick green grass with the postmaster's son.

His daughter looked at him and her eyebrows went up in tired forbearance.

"Put your birds to bed?" she asked, humoring him.

"Lucy," he said urgently. "Lucy . . ."

"Well, what is it now?"

"She's in the garden with Steven."

"Now you just sit down and have your tea."

He stumped his feet alternately, thump, thump, on the hollow wooden floor and shouted: "She'll marry him. I'm telling you, she'll be marrying him next!"

His daughter rose swiftly, brought him a cup, set him a plate.

"I don't want any tea. I don't want it, I tell you."

"Now, now," she crooned. "What's wrong with it? Why not?"

"She's eighteen. Eighteen!"

"I was married at seventeen and I never regretted it."

"Liar," he said. "Liar. Then you should regret it. Why do you make your girls marry? It's you who do it. What do you do it for? Why?"

"The other three have done fine. They've three fine husbands. Why not Alice?"

"She's the last," he mourned. "Can't we keep her a bit longer?"

"Come, now, Dad. She'll be down the road, that's all. She'll be here every day to see you."

"But it's not the same." He thought of the other three girls, transformed inside a few months from charming petulant spoiled children into serious young matrons.

"You never did like it when we married," she said. "Why not? Every time, it's the same. When I got married you made me feel like it was something wrong. And my girls the same. You get them all crying and miserable the way you go on. Leave Alice alone. She's happy." She sighed, letting her eyes linger on the sunlit garden. "She'll marry next month. There's no reason to wait."

"You've said they can marry?" he said incredulously.

"Yes, Dad, why not?" she said coldly, and took up her sewing.

His eyes stung, and he went out on to the veranda. Wet spread down over his chin and he took out a handkerchief and mopped his whole face. The garden was empty.

From around the corner came the young couple; but their faces were no longer set against him. On the wrist of the postmaster's son balanced a young pigeon, the light gleaming on its breast.

"For me?" said the old man, letting the drops shake off his chin. "For me?"

"Do you like it?" The girl grabbed his hand and swung on it. "It's for you, Grandad. Steven brought it for you." They hung about him, affectionate, concerned, trying to charm away his wet eyes and his misery. They took his arms and directed him to the shelf of birds, one on each side, enclosing him, petting him, saying worldlessly that nothing would be changed, nothing could change, and that they would be with him always. The bird was proof of it, they said, from their lying happy eyes, as they thrust it on him. "There, Grandad, it's yours. It's for you."

They watched him as he held it on his wrist, stroking its soft, sun-warmed back, watching the wings lift and balance.

"You must shut it up for a bit," said the girl intimately. "Until it knows this is its home."

"Teach your grandmother to suck eggs," growled the old man.

Released by his half-deliberate anger, they fell back, laughing at him. "We're glad you like it." They moved off, now serious and full of purpose, to the gate, where they hung, backs to him, talking quietly. More than anything could, their grown-up seriousness shut him out, making him alone; also, it quietened him, took the sting out of their tumbling like puppies on the grass. They had forgotten him again. Well, so they should, the old man reassured himself, feeling his throat clotted with tears, his lips trembling. He held the new bird to his face, for the caress of its silken feathers. Then he shut it in a box and took out his favorite.

"*Now* you can go," he said aloud. He held it poised, ready for flight, while he looked down the garden towards the boy and the girl. Then, clenched in the pain of loss, he lifted the bird on his wrist, and watched it soar. A whir, and a spatter of wings, and a cloud of birds rose into the evening from the dovecote.

At the gate Alice and Steven forgot their talk and watched the birds.

On the veranda, that woman, his daughter, stood gazing, her eyes shaded with a hand that still held her sewing.

It seemed to the old man that the whole afternoon had stilled to watch his gesture of self-command, that even the leaves of the trees had stopped shaking.

Dry-eyed and calm, he let his hands fall to his sides and stood erect, staring up into the sky.

The cloud of shining silver birds flew up and up, with a shrill cleaving of wings, over the dark ploughed land and the darker belts of trees and the bright folds of grass, until they floated high in the sunlight, like a cloud of motes of dust.

They wheeled in a wide circle, tilting their wings so there was flash after flash of light, and one after another they dropped from the sunshine of the upper sky to shadow, one after another, returning to the shadowed earth over trees and grass and field, returning to the valley and the shelter of night.

The garden was all a fluster and a flurry of returning birds. Then silence, and the sky was empty.

The old man turned, slowly, taking his time; he lifted his eyes to smile proudly down the garden at his granddaughter. She was staring at him. She did not smile. She was wide-eyed, and pale in the cold shadow, and he saw the tears run shivering off her face.

Responding

1. What is the goal of the grandfather? Does he succeed or fail in the pursuit of his goal? Why?

2. Explain the irony of each of the following:
   a) The grandfather's thoughts as he looks at his daughter, "They were caught and finished, both of them, but the girl was still running free." (page 206)
   b) The emotional reactions of the old man and his granddaughter in the concluding paragraph (page 209).

3. This story uses symbols effectively. What is the relationship between the birds and the human characters in the story? How are those connections supported by a) the title, b) plot, and c) diction?

4. Are the grandfather's fears and objections understandable and/or justified? Or is he simply a meddlesome old man? Comment.

5. Why is the story narrated from the grandfather's point of view? How would the story be changed if it were told from the daughter's or granddaughter's perspective? Would it still work? Why or why not?

6. Extend the story by writing follow-up dialogue for the old man and his granddaughter after he releases the birds.

7. Recall a moment when you had to "let go" of someone or something precious to you. Describe how you felt at the time and how things finally turned out for you.

Student notes, page 251

Will Stanton

BARNEY

Place: a desolate island. Plot: a bizarre experiment. Object: to increase the intelligence of a very special rat.

A *ugust 30th.* We are alone on the island now, Barney and I. It was something of a jolt to have to sack Tayloe after all these years, but I had no alternative. The petty vandalisms I could have forgiven, but when he tried to poison Barney out of simple malice, he was standing in the way of scientific progress. That I cannot condone.

I can only believe the attempt was made while under the influence of alcohol, it was so clumsy. The poison container was overturned and a trail of powder led to Barney's dish. Tayloe's defence was of the flimsiest. He denied it. Who else then?

September 2nd. I am taking a calmer view of the Tayloe affair. The monastic life here must have become too much for him. That, and the abandonment of his precious guinea pigs. He insisted to the last that they were better-suited than Barney to my experiments. They were more his speed, I'm afraid. He was an earnest and willing worker, but something of a clod, poor fellow.

At last I have complete freedom to carry on my work without the mute reproaches of Tayloe. I can only ascribe his violent antagonism toward Barney to jealousy. And now that he has gone, how much happier Barney appears to be! I have given him complete run of the place, and what sport it is to observe how his newly awakened intellectual curiosity carries him about. After only two weeks of glutamic acid treatments, he has become interested in my library, dragging the books from the shelves, and going over them page by page. I am certain he knows there is some knowledge to be gained from them had he but the key.

September 8th. For the past two days I have had to keep Barney confined and how he hates it. I am afraid that when my experiments are completed I shall have to do away with Barney. Ridiculous as it may sound there is still the possibility that he might be able to communicate his intelligence to others of his kind. However small the chance may be, the risk is too great to ignore. Fortunately there is, in the basement, a vault built with the idea of keeping vermin out, and it will serve equally well to keep Barney in.

September 9th. Apparently I have spoken too soon. This morning I let him out to frisk around a bit before commencing a new series of tests. After a quick survey of the room he returned to his cage, sprang up on the door handle, removed the key with his teeth, and before I could stop him, he was out the window. By the time I reached the yard I spied him on the coping of the well, and I arrived on the spot only in time to hear the key splash into the water below.

I own I am somewhat embarrassed. It is the only key. The door is locked. Some valuable papers are in separate compartments inside the vault. Fortunately, although the well is over forty feet deep, there are only a few feet of water in the bottom, so the retrieving of the key does not present an insurmountable obstacle. But I must admit Barney has won the first round.

September 10th. I have had a rather shaking experience, and once more in a minor clash with Barney I have come off second-best. In this instance I will admit he played the hero's role and may even have saved my life.

In order to facilitate my descent into the well I knotted a length of three-quarter-inch rope at one-foot intervals to make a rude ladder. I reached the bottom easily enough, but after only a few minutes of groping for the key, my flashlight gave out and I returned to the surface. A few feet from the top I heard excited squeaks from Barney, and upon obtaining ground level I observed that the rope was almost completely severed. Apparently it had chafed against the edge of the masonry and the little fellow perceiving my plight had been doing his utmost to warn me.

I have now replaced that section of rope and arranged some old sacking beneath it to prevent a recurrence of the accident. I have replenished the batteries in my flashlight and am now prepared for the final descent. These few moments I have taken off to give myself a breathing spell and to bring my journal up to date. Perhaps I should fix myself a sandwich as I may be down there longer than seems likely at the moment.

September 11th. Poor Barney is dead an soon I shell be the same. He was a wonderful ratt and life without him is knot worth livving. If anybody reeds this please do not disturb anything on the island but leeve it like it is as a shryn to Barney, espehilly the old well. Do not look for my body as I will caste myself into the see. You mite bring a couple of young ratts and leeve them as a living memorial to Barney. Females—no males. I sprayned my wrist is why this is written so bad. This is my laste will. Do what I say an don't come back or disturb anything after you bring the young ratts like I said. Just females.

Goodby

Responding

1. Referring to the Sept. 11th entry, explain what has happened since the previous entry.

2. On what grounds is Tayloe fired? How does the protagonist rationalize Tayloe's dismissal?

3. What is the real cause for the dismissal? What other foreshadowing is there of the surprise ending?

4. Find three examples of irony contained in the last two paragraphs of the story.

5. What familiar conventions (patterns, rules) of the science fiction story and the fantasy story does "Barney" contain?

6. Why is the story written in journal form? Would the story have worked any other way? Discuss.

7. Using the point of view and style of the Sept. 11th entry, write a humorous conclusion for the scientist's formal report on the results and applications of this intelligence experiment.

Student notes, page 251

Arthur Conan Doyle

THE CROOKED MAN

Colonel Barclay has been found dead in a pool of blood. Nearby, his wife Nancy lies unconscious on the floor. She is accused of murdering her husband. Sherlock Holmes, literature's most famous detective, is called in to investigate.

O ne summer night, a few months after my marriage, I was seated by my own hearth smoking a last pipe and nodding over a novel, for my day's work had been an exhausting one. My wife had already gone upstairs, and the sound of the locking of the door some time before told me that the servants had also retired. I had risen from my seat and was knocking out the ashes of my pipe, when I suddenly heard the clang of the bell.

I looked at the clock. It was a quarter to twelve. This could not be a visitor at so late an hour. A patient, evidently, and possibly an all-night sitting. With a wry face I went out into the hall and opened the door. To my astonishment, it was Sherlock Holmes who stood upon my step.

"Ah, Watson," said he, "I hoped that I might not be too late to catch you."

"My dear fellow, pray come in."

"You look surprised, and no wonder! Relieved, too, I fancy! Hum! you still smoke the Arcadia mixture of your bachelor days, then! There's no mistaking that fluffy ash upon your coat. It's easy to tell that you've been accustomed to wear a uniform, Watson; you'll never pass as a pure-bred civilian as long as you keep that

habit of carrying your handkerchief in your sleeve. Could you put me up tonight?"

"With pleasure."

"You told me that you had bachelor quarters for one, and I see that you have no gentleman visitor at present. Your hat-stand proclaims as much."

"I shall be delighted if you will stay."

"Thank you. I'll find a vacant peg, then. Sorry to see that you've had the British workman in the house. He's a token of evil. Not the drains, I hope?"

"No, the gas."

"Ah! He has left two nail marks from his boot upon your linoleum just where the light strikes it. No, thank you, I had some supper at Waterloo, but I'll smoke a pipe with you with pleasure."

I handed him my pouch, and he seated himself opposite to me, and smoked for some time in silence. I was well aware that nothing but business of importance could have brought him to me at such an hour, so I waited patiently until he should come round to it.

"I see that you are professionally rather busy just now," said he, glancing keenly across at me.

"Yes, I've had a busy day," I answered. "It may seem very foolish in your eyes," I added, "but really I don't know how you deduced it."

Holmes chuckled to himself.

"I have the advantage of knowing your habits, my dear Watson," said he. "When your round is a short one you walk, and when it is a long one you use a hansom. As I perceive that your boots, although used, are by no means dirty, I cannot doubt that you are at present busy enough to justify the hansom."

"Excellent!" I cried.

"Elementary," said he. "It is one of those instances where the reasoner can produce an effect which seems remarkable to his neighbor, because the latter has missed the one little point which is the basis of the deduction. The same may be said, my dear fellow, for the effect of some of these little sketches of yours, which is entirely meretricious, depending as it does upon your retaining in your own hands some factors in the problem which are never imparted to the reader. Now, at present I am in the position of these same readers, for I hold in this hand several threads of one of the strangest cases which ever perplexed a man's brain, and yet I lack the one or two which are needful to complete my theory. But I'll have them, Watson, I'll have them!" His eyes kindled and a slight flush sprang into his thin cheeks. For an instant the veil had lifted upon his keen, intense nature, but for an instant only. When I glanced again his face had resumed the composure which had made so many regard him as a machine rather than a man.

"The problem presents features of interest," said he; "I may even say very exceptional features of interest. I have already looked into the matter, and have come, as I think, within sight of my solution. If you could accompany me in that last step, you might be of considerable service to me."

"I should be delighted."

"Could you go as far as Aldershot tomorrow?"

"I have no doubt Jackson would take my practice."

"Very good. I want to start by the 11:10 from Waterloo."

"That would give me time."

"Then, if you are not sleepy, I will give you a sketch of what has happened and of what remains to be done."

"I was sleepy before you came. I am quite wakeful now."

"I will compress the story as far as may be done without omitting anything vital to the case. It is conceivable that you may even have read some account of the matter. It is the supposed murder of Colonel Barclay, of the Royal Mallows, at Aldershot, which I am investigating."

"I have heard nothing of it."

"It has not excited much attention yet, except locally. The facts are only two days old. Briefly they are these:

"The Royal Mallows is, as you know, one of the most famous Irish regiments in the British Army. It did wonders both in the Crimea and the Mutiny, and has since that time distinguished itself upon every possible occasion. It was commanded up to Monday night by James Barclay, a gallant veteran, who started as a full private, was raised to commissioned rank for his bravery at the time of the Mutiny, and so lived to command the regiment in which he had once carried a musket.

"Colonel Barclay had married at the time when he was a sergeant, and his wife, whose maiden name was Miss Nancy Devoy, was the daughter of a former color-sergeant in the same corps.

There was, therefore, as can be imagined, some little social friction when the young couple (for they were still young) found themselves in their new surroundings. They appear, however, to have quickly adapted themselves, and Mrs. Barclay has always, I understand, been as popular with the ladies of the regiment as her husband was with his brother officers. I may add that she was a woman of great beauty, and that even now, when she has been married for upwards of thirty years, she is still of a striking appearance.

"Colonel Barclay's family life appears to have been a uniformly happy one. Major Murphy, to whom I owe most of my facts, assures me that he has never heard of any misunderstanding between the pair. On the whole he thinks that Barclay's devotion to his wife was greater than his wife's to Barclay. He was acutely uneasy if he were absent from her for a day. She, on the other hand, though devoted and faithful, was less obtrusively affectionate. But they were regarded in the regiment as the very model of a middle-aged couple. There was absolutely nothing in their mutual relations to prepare people for the tragedy which was to follow.

"Colonel Barclay himself seems to have had some singular traits in his character. He was a dashing, jovial old soldier in his usual mood, but there were occasions on which he seemed to show himself capable of considerable violence and vindictiveness. This side of his nature, however, appears never to have been turned towards his wife. Another fact which had struck Major Murphy, and three out of five of the other officers with whom I conversed, was the singular sort of depression which came upon him at times. As the Major expressed it, the smile had often been struck from his mouth, as if by some invisible hand, when he had been joining in the gaieties and chaff of the mess table. For days on end, when the mood was on him, he had been sunk in the deepest gloom. This and a certain tinge of superstition were the only unusual traits in his character which his brother officers had observed. The latter peculiarity took the form of a dislike of being left alone, especially after dark. This puerile feature in a nature which was conspicuously manly had often given rise to comment and conjecture.

"The first battalion of the Royal Mallows (which is the old 117th) has been stationed at Aldershot for some years. The married officers live out of barracks, and the Colonel has during all this time occupied a villa called Lachine, about half a mile from the North

Camp. The house stands in its own grounds, but the west side of it is not more than thirty yards from the high road. A coachman and two maids form the staff of servants. These, with their master and mistress, were the sole occupants of Lachine, for the Barclays had no children, nor was it usual for them to have resident visitors.

"Now for the events at Lachine between nine and ten on the evening of last Monday.

"Mrs. Barclay was, it appears, a member of the Roman Catholic Church, and had interested herself very much in the establishment of the Guild of St. George, which was formed in connection with the Watt Street Chapel for the purpose of supplying the poor with cast-off clothing. A meeting of the Guild had been held that evening at eight, and Mrs. Barclay had hurried over her dinner in order to be present at it. When leaving the house, she was heard by the coachman to make some commonplace remark to her husband, and to assure him that she would be back before long. She then called for Miss Morrison, a young lady who lives in the next villa, and the two went off together to their meeting. It lasted forty minutes, and at a quarter past nine Mrs. Barclay returned home, having left Miss Morrison at her door as she passed.

"There is a room which is used as a morning-room at Lachine. This faces the road, and opens by a large glass folding door on to the lawn. The lawn is thirty yards across, and is only divided from the highway by a low wall with an iron rail above it. It was into this room that Mrs. Barclay went upon her return. The blinds were not down, for the room was seldom used in the evening, but Mrs. Barclay herself lit the lamp and then rang the bell, asking Jane Stewart, the housemaid, to bring her a cup of tea, which was quite contrary to her usual habits. The Colonel had been sitting in the dining-room, but hearing that his wife had returned, he joined her in the morning-room. The coachman saw him cross the hall, and enter it. He was never seen again alive.

"The tea which had been ordered was brought up at the end of ten minutes, but the maid, as she approached the door, was surprised to hear the voices of her master and mistress in furious altercation. She knocked without receiving any answer, and even turned the handle, but only to find that the door was locked upon the inside. Naturally enough, she ran down to tell the cook, and the two women with the coachman came up into the hall and listened to the dispute which was still raging. They all agree that only two voices were to be heard, those of Barclay and his wife. Barclay's remarks were subdued and abrupt, so that none of them were audible to the listeners. The lady's, on the other hand, were most bitter, and, when she raised her voice, could be plainly heard. "You coward!" she repeated over and over again. "What can be done now? Give back my life. I will never so much as breathe the same air as you again! You coward! You coward!" Those were scraps of her conversation, ending in a sudden dreadful cry in the man's voice, with a crash, and a piercing scream from the woman. Convinced that some tragedy had occurred, the coachman rushed to the door and strove to force it, while scream after scream issued from within. He was unable, however, to make his way in, and the maids were too distracted with fear to be of any assistance to him. A sudden thought struck him, however, and he ran through the hall door and round to the lawn, upon which the long French windows opened. One side of the window was open, which I understand was quite usual in the summer-time, and he passed without difficulty into the room. His mistress had ceased to scream, and was stretched insensible upon a couch, while with his feet tilted over the side of an armchair, and his head upon the ground near the corner of the fender, was lying the unfortunate soldier, stone dead, in a pool of his own blood.

"Naturally the coachman's first thought, on finding that he could do nothing for his master, was to open the door. But here an unexpected and singular difficulty presented itself. The key was not on the inner side of the door, nor could he find it anywhere in the room. He went out again, therefore, through the window, and having obtained the help of a policeman and of a medical man, he returned. The lady, against whom naturally the strongest suspicion rested, was removed to her room, still in a state of insensibility. The Colonel's body was then placed upon the sofa, and a careful examination made of the scene of the tragedy.

"The injury from which the unfortunate veteran was suffering was found to be a ragged cut, some two inches long, at the back part of his head, which had evidently been caused by a violent blow from a blunt weapon. Nor was it difficult to guess what that weapon may have been. Upon the floor, close to the body, was lying a singular club of hard carved wood with a bone handle. The Colonel possessed a varied collection of weapons brought from the different countries in which he had fought, and it is conjectured by the police that this club was among his trophies. The servants deny having seen it before, but among the numerous curiosities in the house it is possible that it may have been overlooked. Nothing else of importance was discovered in the room by the police, save the inexplicable fact that neither upon Mrs. Barclay's person, nor upon that of the victim, nor in any part of the room was the missing key to be found. The door had eventually to be opened by a locksmith from Aldershot.

"That was the state of things, Watson, when upon the Tuesday morning I, at the request of Major Murphy, went down to Aldershot to supplement the efforts of the police. I think you will acknowledge that the problem was already one of interest, but my observations soon made me realize that it was in truth much more extraordinary than would at first sight appear.

"Before examining the room I cross-questioned the servants, but only succeeded in eliciting the facts which I have already stated. One other detail of interest was remembered by Jane Stewart, the housemaid. You will remember that on hearing the sound of the quarrel she descended and returned with the other servants. On that first occasion, when she was alone, she says that the voices of her master and mistress were sunk so low that she could hear hardly anything, and judged by their tones, rather than their words, that they had fallen out. On my pressing her, however, she remembered that she heard the word 'David' uttered twice by the lady. The point is of the utmost importance as guiding us towards the reason of the sudden quarrel. The Colonel's name, you remember, was James.

"There was one thing in the case which had made the deepest impression both upon the servants and the police. This was the contortion of the Colonel's face. It had set, according to their account, into the most dreadful expression of fear and horror which a human countenance is capable of assuming. More than one person fainted at the mere sight of him, so terrible was the effect. It was quite certain that he had foreseen his fate, and that it had caused him the utmost horror. This, of course, fitted in well enough with the police theory, if the Colonel could have seen his wife making a murderous attack upon him. Nor was the fact of the wound being on the back of his head a fatal objection to this, as he might have turned to avoid the blow. No information could be got from the lady herself, who was temporarily insane from an acute attack of brain fever.

"From the police I learned that Miss Morrison, who, you remember, went out that evening with Mrs. Barclay, denied having any knowledge of what it was which had caused the ill-humor in which her companion had returned.

"Having gathered these facts, Watson, I smoked several pipes over them, trying to separate those which were crucial from others which were merely incidental. There could be no question that the most distinctive and suggestive point in the case was the singular disappearance of the door key. A most careful search had failed to discover it in the room. Therefore, it must have been taken from it. But neither the Colonel nor the Colonel's wife could have taken it. That was perfectly clear. Therefore, a third person must have entered the room. And that third person could only have come through the window. It seemed to me that a careful examination of the room and the lawn might possibly reveal some traces of this mysterious individual. You know my methods, Watson. There was not one of them which I did not apply to the inquiry. And it ended by my discovering traces, but very different ones from those which I had expected. There had been a man in the room, and he had crossed the lawn coming from the road. I was able to obtain five very clear impressions of his footmarks—one on the roadway itself, at the point where he had climbed the low wall, two on the lawn, and two very faint ones upon the stained boards near the window where he had entered. He had apparently rushed across the lawn, for his toe marks were much deeper than his heels. But it was not the man who surprised me. It was his companion."

"His companion!"

Holmes pulled a large sheet of tissue paper out of his pocket and carefully unfolded it upon his knee.

"What do you make of that?" he asked.

The paper was covered with tracings of the footmarks of some small animal. It had five well-marked footpads, an indication of long nails, and the whole print might be nearly as large as a dessert spoon.

"It's a dog," said I.

"Did you ever hear of a dog running up a curtain? I found distinct traces that this creature had done so."

"A monkey, then?"

"But it is not the print of a monkey."

"What can it be, then?"

"Neither dog, nor cat, nor monkey, nor any creature that we are familiar with. I have tried to reconstruct it from the measurements. Here are four prints where the beast has been standing motionless. You see that it is no less than fifteen inches from fore foot to hind. Add to that the length of neck and head, and you get a creature not much less than two feet long—probably more if there is any tail. But now observe this other measurement. The animal has been moving, and we have the length of its stride. In each case it is only about three inches. You have an indication, you see, of a long body with very short legs attached to it. It has not been considerate enough to leave any of its hair behind it. But its general shape must be what I have indicated, and it can run up a curtain and is carnivorous."

"How do you deduce that?"

"Because it ran up the curtain. A canary's cage was hanging in the window, and its aim seems to have been to get at the bird."

"Then what was the beast?"

"Ah, if I could give it a name it might go a long way towards solving the case. On the whole it was probably some creature of the weasel or stoat tribe—and yet it is larger than any of these that I have seen."

"But what had it to do with the crime?"

"That also is still obscure. But we have learned a good deal, you perceive. We know that a man stood in the road looking at the quarrel between the Barclays—the blinds were up and the room lighted. We know also that he ran across the lawn, entered the room, accompanied by a strange animal, and that he either struck the Colonel, or, as is equally possible, that the Colonel fell down from sheer fright at the sight of him, and cut his head on the corner of the fender. Finally, we have the curious fact that the intruder carried away the key with him when he left."

"Your discoveries seem to have left the business more obscure than it was before," said I.

"Quite so. They undoubtedly showed that the affair was much

deeper than was at first conjectured. I thought the matter over, and I came to the conclusion that I must approach the case from another aspect. But really, Watson, I am keeping you up, and I might just as well tell you all this on our way to Aldershot tomorrow."

"Thank you, you've gone rather too far to stop."

"It was quite certain that when Mrs. Barclay left the house at half past seven she was on good terms with her husband. She was never, as I think I have said, ostentatiously affectionate, but she was heard by the coachman chatting with the Colonel in a friendly fashion. Now, it was equally certain that immediately on her return she had gone to the room in which she was least likely to see her husband, had flown to tea, as an agitated woman will, and, finally, on his coming in to her, had broken into violent recriminations. Therefore, something had occurred between seven-thirty and nine o'clock which had completely altered her feelings towards him. But Miss Morrison had been with her during the whole of that hour and a half. It was absolutely certain, therefore, in spite of her denial, that she must know something of the matter.

"My first conjecture was that possibly there had been some passages between this young woman and the old soldier, which the former had now confessed to the wife. That would account for the angry return and also for the girl's denial that anything had occurred. Nor would it be entirely incompatible with most of the words overheard. But there was the reference to David, and there was the known affection of the Colonel for his wife to weigh against it, to say nothing of the tragic intrusion of this other man, which might, of course, be entirely disconnected with what had gone before. It was not easy to pick one's steps, but on the whole I was inclined to dismiss the idea that there had been anything between the Colonel and Miss Morrison, but more than ever convinced that the young lady held the clue as to what it was which had turned Mrs. Barclay to hatred of her husband. I took the obvious course, therefore, of calling upon Miss Morrison, of explaining to her that I was perfectly certain that she held the facts in her possession, and of assuring her that her friend, Mrs. Barclay, might find herself in the dock upon a capital charge unless the matter were cleared up.

"Miss Morrison is a little, ethereal slip of a girl, with timid eyes and blonde hair, but I found her by no means wanting in shrewdness and common sense. She sat thinking for some time after I had spoken, and then turning to me with a brisk air of resolution, she broke into a remarkable statement, which I will condense for your benefit.

" 'I promised my friend that I would say nothing of the matter, and a promise is a promise,' said she. 'But if I can really help her when so serious a charge is made against her, and when her own mouth, poor darling, is closed by illness, then I think I am absolved from my promise. I will tell you exactly what happened on Monday evening.

" 'We were returning from the Watt Street Mission, about a quarter to nine o'clock. On our way we had to pass through Hudson Street, which is a very quiet thoroughfare. There is only one lamp in it upon the left-hand side, and as we approached this lamp I saw a man coming towards us with his back very bent, and something like a box slung over one of his shoulders. He appeared to be deformed, for he carried his head low, and walked with his knees bent. We were passing him when he raised his face to look at us in the circle of light thrown by the lamp, and as he did so he stopped and screamed out in a dreadful voice, "My God, it's Nancy!" Mrs. Barclay turned as white as death, and would have fallen down had the dreadful-looking creature not caught hold of her. I was going to call for the police, but she, to my surprise, spoke quite civilly to the fellow.

" 'I thought you had been dead this thirty years, Henry,' said she, in a shaking voice.

" 'So I have,' said he and it was awful to hear the tones that he said it in. He had a very dark, fearsome face, and a gleam in his eyes that comes back to me in my dreams. His hair and whiskers were shot with grey, and his face was all crinkled and puckered like a withered apple.

" 'Just walk on a little way, dear,' said Mrs Barclay. 'I want to have a word with this man. There is nothing to be afraid of.' She tried to speak boldly, but she was still deadly pale, and could hardly get her words out for the trembling of her lips.

" 'I did as she asked me, and they talked together for a few minutes. Then she came down the street with her eyes blazing, and I saw the crippled wretch standing by the lamp-post and shaking his clenched fists in the air, as if he were mad with rage. She never said a word until we were at the door here, when she took me by the hand and begged me to tell no one what had happened. "It is an old acquaintance of mine who has come down in the world," said she. When I promised her that I would say nothing she kissed me, and I have never seen her since. I have told you now the whole truth, and if I withheld it from the police it is because I did not realize then the danger in which my dear friend stood. I know that it can only be to her advantage that everything should be known.'

"There was her statement, Watson, and to me, as you can imagine, it was like a light on a dark night. Everything which had been disconnected before began at once to assume its true place, and I had a shadowy presentiment of the whole sequence of events. My next step obviously was to find the man who had produced such a remarkable impression upon Mrs. Barclay. If he were still in Aldershot it should not be a very difficult matter. There are not such a very great number of civilians, and a deformed man was sure to have attracted attention. I spent a day in the search, and by evening—this very evening, Watson—I had run him down. The man's name is Henry Wood, and he lives in lodgings in the same street in which the ladies met him. He has only been five days in the place. In the character of a registration agent I had a most interesting gossip with his landlady. The man is by trade a conjurer and performer, going round the canteens, after nightfall, and giving a little entertainment at each. He carries some creature about with him in his box, about which the landlady seemed to be in considerable trepidation, for she had never seen an animal like it. He uses it in some of his tricks, according to her account. So much the woman was able to tell me, and also that it was a wonder the man lived, seeing how twisted he was, and that he spoke in a strange tongue sometimes, and that for the last two nights she had heard him groaning and weeping in his bedroom. He was all right as far as money went, but in his deposit he had given her what looked like a bad florin. She showed it to me, Watson, and it was an Indian rupee.

"So now, my dear fellow, you see exactly how we stand and why it is I want you. It is perfectly plain that after the ladies parted from this man he followed them at a distance, that he saw the quarrel between husband and wife through the window, that he rushed in, and that the creature which he carred in his box got loose. That is all very certain. But he is the only person in this world who can tell us exactly what happened in that room."

"And you intend to ask him?"

"Most certainly—but in the presence of a witness."

"And I am the witness?"

"If you will be so good. If he can clear the matter up, well and good. If he refuses, we have no alternative but to apply for a warrant."

"But how do you know he will be there when we return?"

"You may be sure that I took some precautions. I have one of my Baker Street boys mounting guard over him who would stick to him like a burr, go where he might. We shall find him in Hudson Street tomorrow, Watson; and meanwhile I should be the criminal myself if I kept you out of bed any longer."

It was midday when we found ourselves at the scene of the tragedy, and, under my companion's guidance, we made our way at once to Hudson Street. In spite of his capacity for concealing his emotions I could easily see that Holmes was in a state of suppressed excitement, while I was myself tingling with that half-sporting, half-intellectual pleasure which I invariably experienced when I associated myself with him in his investigations.

"This is the street," said he, as he turned into a short thoroughfare lined with plain, two-storeyed brick houses—"Ah! here is Simpson to report."

"He's in all right, Mr. Holmes," cried a small street boy, running up to us.

"Good, Simpson!" said Holmes, patting him on the head. "Come along, Watson. This is the house." He sent in his card with a message that he had come on important business, and a moment later we were face to face with the man whom we had come to see. In spite of the warm weather he was crouching over a fire and the little room was like an oven. The man sat all twisted and huddled in his chair in a way which gave an indescribable impression of deformity, but the face which he turned towards us, though worn and swarthy, must at some time have been remarkable for its beauty. He looked suspiciously at us now out of yellow-shot bilious eyes, and, without speaking or rising, he waved towards two chairs.

"Mr. Henry Wood, late of India, I believe?" said Holmes, affably. "I've come over this little matter of Colonel Barclay's death."

"What should I know about that?"

"That's what I wanted to ascertain. You know, I suppose, that unless the matter is cleared up, Mrs. Barclay, who is an old friend of yours, will in all probability be tried for murder?"

The man gave a violent start.

"I don't know who you are," he cried, "nor how you come to know what you do know, but will you swear that this is true that you tell me?"

"Why, they are only waiting for her to come to her senses to arrest her."

"My God! Are you in the police yourself?"

"No."

"What business is it of yours, then?"

"It's every man's business to see justice done."

"You can take my word that she is innocent."

"Then you are guilty?"

"No, I am not."

"Who killed Colonel James Barclay, then?"

"It was a just Providence that killed him. But mind you this, that if I had knocked his brains out, as it was in my heart to do, he would have had no more than his due from my hands. If his own guilty conscience had not struck him down, it is likely enough that I might have had his blood upon my soul. You want me to tell the story? Well, I don't know why I shouldn't, for there's no cause for me to be ashamed of it.

"It was in this way, sir. You see me now with my back like a camel and my ribs all awry, but there was a time when Corporal Henry Wood was the smartest man in the 117th Foot. We were in India then, in cantonments, at a place we'll call Bhurtee. Barclay, who died the other day, was sergeant in the same company as myself, and the belle of the regiment—aye, and the finest girl that ever had the breath of life between her lips—was Nancy Devoy, the daughter of the colour-sergeant. There were two men who loved her, and one whom she loved; and you'll smile when you look at this poor thing huddled before the fire, and hear me say that it was for my good looks that she loved me.

"Well, though I had her heart her father was set upon her marrying Barclay. I was a harum-scarum, reckless lad, and he had

had an education, and was already marked for the sword-belt. But the girl held true to me, and it seemed that I would have had her, when the Mutiny broke out, and all hell was loose in the country.

"We were shut up in Bhurtee, the regiment of us, with half a battery of artillery, a company of Sikhs, and a lot of civilians and women-folk. There were ten thousand rebels round us, and they were as keen as a set of terriers round a rat cage. About the second week of it our water gave out, and it was a question whether we could communicate with General Neill's column, which was moving up country. It was our only chance, for we could not hope to fight our way out with all the women and children, so I volunteered to go out and warn General Neill of our danger. My offer was accepted, and I talked it over with Sergeant Barclay, who was supposed to know the ground better than any other man, and who drew up a route by which I might get through the rebel lines. At ten o'clock the same night I started off upon my journey. There were a thousand lives to save, but it was of only one that I was thinking when I dropped over the wall that night.

"My way ran down a dried-up watercourse, which we hoped would screen me from the enemy's sentries, but as I crept round the corner of it I walked right into six of them, who were crouching down in the dark waiting for me. In an instant I was stunned with a blow, and bound hand and foot. But the real blow was to my heart and not to my head, for as I came to and listened to as much as I could understand of their talk, I heard enough to tell me that my comrade, the very man who had arranged the way I was to take, had betrayed me by means of a native servant into the hands of the enemy.

"Well, there's no need for me to dwell on that part of it. You know now what James Barclay was capable of. Bhurtee was relieved by Neill next day, but the rebels took me away with them in their retreat, and it was many a long year before ever I saw a white face again. I was tortured, and tried to get away, and was captured and tortured again. You can see for yourselves the state in which I was left. Some of them that fled into Nepal took me with them, and then afterwards I was up past Darjeeling. The hill-folk up there murdered the rebels who had me, and I became their slave for a time until I escaped, but instead of going south I had to go north, until I found myself among the Afghans. There I wandered about for many a year, and at last came back to the Punjab, where I lived mostly among the natives, and picked up a living by the conjuring tricks that I had learned. What use was it for me, a wretched cripple, to go back to England, or to make myself known to my old comrades? Even my wish for revenge would not make me do that. I had rather that Nancy and my old pals should think of Harry Wood as having died with a straight back, than see him living and crawling with a stick like a chimpanzee. They never doubted that I was dead, and I meant that they never should. I heard that Barclay had married Nancy, and that he was rapidly rising in the regiment, but even that did not make me speak.

"But when one gets old, one has a longing for home. For years I've been dreaming of the bright green fields and the hedges of England. At last I determined to see them before I died. I saved enough to bring me across, and then I came here where the soldiers are, for I know their ways, and how to amuse them, and so earn enough to keep me."

"Your narrative is most interesting," said Sherlock Holmes. "I have already heard of your meeting with Mrs. Barclay and your mutual recognition. You then, as I understand, followed her home and saw through the window an altercation between her husband and her, in which she doubtless cast his conduct to you in his teeth. Your own feelings overcame you, and you ran across the lawn, and broke in upon them."

"I did, sir, and at the sight of me he looked as I have never seen a man look before, and over he went with his head on the fender. But he was dead before he fell. I read death on his face as plain as I can read that text over the fire. The bare sight of me was like a bullet through his guilty heart."

"And then?"

"Then Nancy fainted, and I caught up the key of the door from her hand, intending to unlock it and get help. But as I was doing it it seemed to me better to leave it alone and get away, for the thing might look black against me, and anyway my secret would be out if I were taken. In my haste I thrust the key into my pocket, and dropped my stick while I was chasing Teddy, who had run up the curtain. When I got him into his box, from which he had slipped, I was off as fast as I could run."

"Who's Teddy?" asked Holmes.

The man leaned over and pulled up the front of a kind of hutch in the corner. In an instant out there slipped a beautiful reddish-brown creature, thin, and lithe, with the legs of a stoat, a long thin nose, and a pair of the finest red eyes that ever I saw in an animal's head.

"It's a mongoose!" I cried.

"Well, some call them that, and some call them ichneumon," said the man. "Snake-catcher is what I call them, and Teddy is amazing quick on cobras. I have one here without the fangs, and Teddy catches it every night to please the folk in the canteen. Any other point, sir?"

"Well, we may have to apply to you again if Mrs. Barclay should prove to be in serious trouble."

"In that case, of course, I'd come forward."

"But if not, there is no object in raking up this scandal against a dead man, foully as he has acted. You have, at least, the satisfaction of knowing that for thirty years of his life his conscience bitterly reproached him for his wicked deed. Ah, there goes Major Murphy on the other side of the street. Good-bye, Wood; I want to learn if anything has happened since yesterday."

We were in time to overtake the Major before he reached the corner.

"Ah, Holmes" he said, "I suppose you have heard that all this fuss has come to nothing?"

"What, then?"

"The inquest is just over. The medical evidence showed conclusively that death was due to apoplexy. You see, it was quite a simple case after all."

"Oh, remarkably superficial," said Holmes, smiling. "Come, Watson, I don't think we shall be wanted in Aldershot any more."

"There's one thing," said I, as we walked down to the station; "if the husband's name was James, and the other was Henry, what was this talk about David?"

"That one word, my dear Watson, should have told me the whole story had I been the ideal reasoner which you are so fond of depicting. It was evidently a term of reproach."

"Of reproach?"

"Yes, David strayed a little now and then, you know, and on one occasion in the same direction as Sergeant James Barclay. You remember the small affair of Uriah and Bathsheba? My Biblical knowledge is a trifle rusty, I fear, but you will find the story in the first or second of Samuel."

Responding

1. Check the definition of mystery story in the Glossary. Then find examples in this story of the six typical parts of a mystery story.

2. Whodunits contain genuine evidence as well as "red herrings" (false clues and suspects). What are the "red herrings" of this mystery? What evidence foreshadows the actual cause of Colonel Barclay's death?

3. What is the significance of the allusion to David (page 222)? Who is the "crooked man" of the title?

4. Who tells the story? What is his relationship to the protagonist? What advantages are there to using this narrative point of view?

5. a) What characteristics of fictional detectives does Holmes have? What methods does he use to solve the mystery?
   b) In two paragraphs, compare and contrast Holmes with a modern detective you have seen in the movies or on television.

6. The setting, atmosphere, and local color of this whodunit are well-developed. Where and when does this story take place? How can you tell?

7. Write a newspaper account of the case as it might have appeared in a sensationalistic newspaper of that time. Include imagined excerpts of interviews with several of the story's characters.

Student notes, page 252

Maara Haas

A WAY OUT
OF THE FOREST

The search for a better life takes two young children into a twilight world of experience.

R ouga lay on her side and listened. Aside from the smacking of Grandfather's toothless gums and the scratching of sparrows along the eaves, there was no sound in the room. Arnie slept quietly beside her.

After the big storm five years ago, sparrows had taken to building their nests under the loosened tarpaper roof. When the March wind swept over Grand Marais the nests unravelled and dripped over the doorway of the house. Rouga watched the thin evening light streaking through the small window beaded with the limestone droppings of the sparrows. Barely touching the cold linoleum floor, the dull metal of the boxstove, the sun fell back and the room was again dark.

Arnie had wriggled down past the pillow. His cheeks, pressing on a mattress button, pouted his mouth like one of the cherubs blowing four winds from the four corners of the world map hanging in the settlement schoolhouse. As usual, he managed to wrap the blanket around him, leaving her the tail end with Daddy's number, R177599.

Rouga pulled the army greatcoat over their heads to make a tent. The wool of the coat against her face was damp and warm. I suppose there are different kinds of dark, she thought. It was dark under the folds of the coat but somehow comforting and not like going to the outhouse by herself when it was scary dark.

"It doesn't smell so good in here," said Arnie in a muffled voice:

"I can't breathe."

The smell came from the baby's pee, soaked and dried into the mattress. Rouga was used to the smell but she was wary of the centre of the bed where Arnie was in the habit of pushing her, the rusty metal slat left against her spine. "I'm on the railroad track again," she complained: "Move."

Almost new, the davenport was nicer than anything in Eaton's catalogue, the applegreen bedspread sprinkled with bouquets of wildflowers and a frill across the bottom to hide the stuffings. It was the only bed in the settlement that opened and closed like a sandwich and everybody had a try at it until the magic spring broke. Now it lay flat all the time. When I get married, Rouga vowed silently. I'll have a house with two rooms and two davenports.

Arnie was impatient: "How long are we going to stay here? I'm tired of sleeping."

"You can't leave the tent," said Rouga, tying the flap of the greatcoat together. "It's winter outside. "The snow is forty feet deep on the prairie and the men have deserted. Snowshoes could save us but Daddy took the only pair to the bush and he won't be back till there's pie in the sky. Mummy says it's hopeless and Grandfather is too busy talking to the wind and the sky to be bothered with us."

"I'm awfully hungry," said Arnie mournfully.

Rouga lifted the greatcoat aside and pointed in the direction of the cupboard: "There's a cache of food, bread and suet, maybe tea, buried just three yards from our tent. Shall we risk it?"

"I hate bread and suet," Arnie protested. "I want a sugar doughnut and some canned milk. Or jam. I saw Mummy hide it."

"The jam is for Grandfather, don't you know?" Rouga said in a scolding tone: "If you're that fussy, you'll have to wait for the Government Relief."

"How long is that?" asked Arnie.

Rouga deliberated. "Five years, I guess."

"OK," said Arnie, satisfied. "I'll wait. But in the meantime I wouldn't mind a piece of bread and suet. Please." He added the last for good measure. Rouga was very strict for manners, like Mummy. He crawled out of the tent and tucked the sleeves of the greatcoat into the pockets.

"To keep out the prairie wolves," he said with a grin: "Shall we bring our supplies into the tent?"

Rouga looked out the window. She licked her finger and held it up to the wind: "South, south-east. The blizzard has run its course. Let's sit at the top of that snowy hill beside the campfire." They carried their food to the boxstove and sat down.

"I don't like bread and suet," Arnie insisted.

"Just be glad you're alive," answered Rouga.

Arnie's small voice quavered: "You sound just like Daddy." He sniffed: "I think I'm going to cry."

The baby used to cry most of the time. He was soft to hold and the top of his head was feathery with black hair. Rouga missed the baby but she didn't feel sick about it like Mummy, rocking back and forth on her knees, her hands pressed to her chest, and moaning: "Bab-eee, Bab-eee—If you had come another time, another place, how would it be? Would your bones melt like the winter snow, the blood in your veins trickle away in a stream of cold blue water, with nothing to mark your coming and going?—"

"Do you think Mummy will die from New Monia?" asked Arnie.

"I suppose so." Rouga answered: "Everyone in the settlement gets New Monia."

Arnie was curious: "Do other people get it?"

"Not much," said Rouga with a touch of pride: "Only Indians have New Monia. Indians are special for it, Daddy claims."

Arnie put down his bread and suet and thought for a moment: "Will Grandfather die from New Monia?"

"Don't be silly," Rouga replied. "Great men never die. Besides, he's much too old for New Monia."

"At least two hundred and fifty," said Arnie, knowingly: "Grandfather told me he's a white buffalo and the white buffalo is older than anything, I think."

Rouga doubted that Grandfather was the legendary white buffalo, but she knew her Grandfather was very old. His unwrinkled skin was pulled tight over his bones like the skin of caribou stretched in the hot summer sun for drying, as she saw it once in a school history book: *Indian Life with Pictures.* Her teacher said Grandfather wore the Great Robes of Tradition and walked in the Spiritual Light across of the Sun. Maybe that could explain how

Grandfather could go naked across the dark prairie and see his way without a lantern as he paced the night, singing over and over, the sad, thin song: "Where are all our warriors? Why have fences come over our hunting grounds? Enepoka—Enepoka—We are dying."

The river, the muddy shoals and the grasses surrounding them, changed with the seasons. Often torn up by the tide, the grasses floated away, leaving in their place a mud pocket the size of a gopher hole.

Waves left small steps in the sand climbing the riverbank. But the stones in the shallows never moved or changed. There were no rings of water to show that the tides or seasons had touched them or passed over them, and when you took them out of the river, they stayed the same color. And there were other stones, an earth-red colour, sparkling glistening with a thousand eyes, that lost their light, the blood drained out of them when lifted out of water where they stood.

Rouga puzzled the riddle of stones and tides. Were people and stones somehow alike? If you took people to another place, a place they didn't belong, would they change and become something else? Rouga wondered what would happen if she left Grand Marais. Would it be more terrible than New Monia or the fate of the frozen sparrows falling from the eaves?

Arnie had finished his bread. He turned to Rouga with bright, expectant eyes: "Are we going back to the tent now?"

Rouga considered him thoughtfully: "How would you like your very own pot of jam and all the sugar doughnuts you could eat?"

Arnie's eyes grew round with excitement: "I'd like it fine. Do we have to wait for the guvimint relief?"

"No," said Rouga: "We don't have to wait a single minute. Not if we go to the City. God knows what you'll find in the City—isn't that what Daddy says?"

"Is it far?" asked Arnie: "If it's much far, we might not find our way back home."

"That's easy," answered Rouga: "We'll leave a trail of pebbles so we can't get lost."

"A trail of pebbles," repeated Arnie, delighted with the whole idea.

The April night was bare of moon or stars. Dimly within sight, the piercing red and yellow stars of a nuclear power plant broke through the thickened blackness of the sky. Crossing the highway to the other side, Rouga took Arnie's hand in hers.

"When do we come to the enchanted land?" Arnie asked, waiting to be assured: "Is it after the City? I want to see the Pure River with Silver Fish the forests of trees full of rainbow-colored birds the Ancient Turtle and the Great-Great-Grandfather spouting Whales. And see, I nearly forgot to mention the bearded brown Buffalo the funny Beavers with tails like paddles. Let's not miss THEM."

"Oh," said Rouga impatiently. "You can't believe everything Grandfather told us."

They walked quickly, the wind pressing them on. Behind them, the scattering of pebbles was lifted up by the dust and gravel of speeding cars, criss-crossing the stones in opposite directions. A light rain freckled Arnie's trusting, upturned face as he skipped, half ran toward the firecracker of lights exploding on the City.

Responding

1. What is the setting of this story? What is the situation of the family? Give evidence from the selection to support your opinions.

2. What happens in the last four paragraphs of the story? What motivates this action? How does the author make this final action believable?

3. What is the significance of a) the stones b) the pebbles c) the title?

4. "This story is an interesting blend of reality and illusion." Discuss this statement, making reference to the plot, conflict, and setting.

5. Tell about a time from your childhood when you got lost or ran away. Compare your experience to that of the children in the story.

6. Write a brief sequel to the story from Arnie's point of view.

Student notes, page 253

STUDENT NOTES

THE FRIDAY EVERYTHING CHANGED (page 2)

Anne Hart

A contributor to Canadian magazines and anthologies, Anne Hart was born in Winnipeg. She spent her childhood years in Nova Scotia, and then moved to St. John's, Newfoundland, where she presently lives.

Notes

forlornly	unhappily
galvanized	covered with zinc to prevent rust
pirouettings	whirling movements on one foot
transfixed	made motionless

WISH YOU WERE HERE (page 12)

Frank Jones

A columnist for the *Toronto Star*, Frank Jones was born in Luton, England in 1937. Recognized nationally for his reporting, he was a bureau chief in Ottawa and in London, England. Jones credits his sister-in-law for providing the idea for this story, which is reputed to be true.

Notes

arbor	a shaded area formed by trees
gnome	a dwarf supposedly guarding a treasure in his underground home
trundled	rolled along

THE WHALE (page 24)

Yves Thériault

Born in Quebec City in 1915, Yves Thériault was one of the province's most popular and prolific writers. He wrote in many different genres for many different audiences. English Canadians will know him best for his novels *Agaguk* (1958), *N'Tusk* (1968), *Ashini* (1972), and *Agoak* (1979). He died in 1983.

Notes

corroborate	confirm or prove
disconsolate	unhappy
embellished	made more elaborate
imperturbably	not easily upset
obnoxious	very offensive
prissy	overly concerned with being proper
quay	a loading dock for ships, often made of stone
tiller	the handle for turning the rudder of a boat

THE SEA DEVIL *(page 32)*

Arthur Gordon

Arthur Gordon (1912-   ), a freelance writer, is the author of both fiction and nonfiction. He has written about American fighter pilots in World War II (*Fighters Up*, 1945), a famous New York preacher (*Norman Vincent Peale, Minister to Millions*), and the United States missile program (*Countdown for Decision*, 1960).

Notes

atavistic	primitive; resembling a remote ancestor
barnacle	animal having a shell that attaches to rocks, boat bottoms and docks
causeway	raised highway built over water
mullet	kind of edible fish
phosphorescence	glowing light
pilings	beams driven into water or ground
skiff	small, light rowboat

THE FATHER *(Page 42)*

Hugh Garner

Born in England, Hugh Garner (1913-1979) grew up in the poorer sections of downtown Toronto. His career was a varied one: he was once a newspaper copyboy, "rode the rails" during the Depression, and saw action in both the Spanish Civil War and World War II.

Garner was a gravel-voiced, hard-living man who enjoyed story-telling. Many of his stories are about working-class Ontario, and the lives of losers and outsiders. In all, he wrote 17 books and 100 short stories. His *Best Stories* won the 1963 Governor-General's Award for Fiction.

Notes

acquiesced	quietly agreed to; consented to without objections
burlesque	vaudeville that features striptease and comedy sketches
curate	clergyman who assists a pastor or vicar
dais	raised platform for speakers
investiture at Buckingham Palace	formal ceremony giving power and authority to England's king and queen
mollify	appease; soften
over-loquacious	over-talkative
sanctity	holiness; saintliness; godliness

THE CARVED TABLE (page 54)

Mary Peterson

A senior writer at the University of New Hampshire, Mary Peterson makes her home in Kittery Point, Maine. After studying writing at the University of Iowa Writer's Workshop and at the University of New Hampshire, she received the National Endowment for the Arts fellowship grant in fiction and was the winner of an O. Henry award. Her collection of short stories called *Mercy Flights* was published in 1985 and she has had many other stories published in literary quarterlies throughout the United States and Canada.

Notes

Marblehead	popular Massachusetts summer resort town and yachting centre
pontificate	speak pompously
scallops	shell-shaped curves

ALICIA (page 60)

Gabrielle Roy

Born in Manitoba, Gabrielle Roy (1909-1983) spent most of her adult life in Quebec. She is one of Canada's better-known French-Canadian writers, especially recognized for her stories about the poor and about young people growing into a greater awareness of life. One of her novels, *Bonheur d'occasion (The Tin Flute*, 1945) was recently made into a movie.

Notes

abominable	hateful
balsams	trees with shiny dark needles often used for Christmas trees
delineated	outlined
diminutive	small
encumbered	burdened
Judas	allusion to Judas Iscariot, the disciple who betrayed Christ
lucidity	clearness of meaning, as in speech
Petite Misère	affectionate nickname meaning "little trifle"
pliancy	flexibility

THE PARSLEY GARDEN (page 71)

William Saroyan

An American of Armenian background, William Saroyan (1908-1981) was born in Fresno, California. He grew up among many relatives who often appear in his writings. First published at the age of twenty-five, William Saroyan went on to achieve acclaim mostly as a novelist and Pulitzer Prize-winning dramatist. Some of his best-known books are *My Name Is Aram* (1940) *The Human Comedy* (1942) and *Boys and Girls Together* (1963).

Note

Hippodrome	an arena or similar structure for shows or spectacles.

WHO SAID WE ALL HAVE TO TALK ALIKE

Wilma Elizabeth McDaniel   *(page 80)*

Part-Cherokee Indian, Wilma Elizabeth McDaniel was born in 1918 in Oklahoma. Prompted by the Great Depression, in her mid-teens McDaniel moved to California, where she presently lives.

Notes

blowed her stack	colloquial expression for "lost her temper"
coll-oke-ism	colloquialism, meaning expressions limited to one geographical region
Gabriel	one of the seven angels who remain ready to act as God's messenger to mankind
hankered	colloquialism, meaning "longed for"
hock-deep	ankle deep
Ozark	from the mountainous region of Missouri, Arkansas, or Oklahoma
tower of Babel	in the Old Testament, a story explaining the different languages of mankind. Noah's descendants, who spoke the same language, decided to build a city and a tower that would reach heaven. To prevent this and teach them not to be so vain, God caused them to speak different languages.

A MOUNTAIN JOURNEY *(page 90)*

Howard O'Hagan

Howard O'Hagan (1902-1982) was born in Lethbridge, Alberta and lived in Victoria, B.C. His early experiences as a mountain guide in the Rockies are reflected in his short story collection, *The Woman Who Got on at Jasper Station and Other Stories* (1963) and a novel, *Tay John* (1939).

Notes

bannock	a flat round cake made with unleavened flour, salt and water
hoodoo	a strangely shaped formation of earth resulting from erosion
siwashing	an Anglo-Saxon term taken from the French, meaning "to live like a native person"

THE VELDT *(page 100)*

Ray Bradbury

Raymond Douglas Bradbury (1920-   ) is a prominent American science fiction writer. This famous Los Angeles resident's best-known works include the novels *Something Wicked This Way Comes* (1983) *The Martian Chronicles* (1958) and *Fahrenheit 451* (1967), all of which have been made into films.

Bradbury's stories are usually a blend of the macabre and the humorous. He often questions unchecked technological progress as well as humanity's ability to deal with the new worlds offered by science and technology. In "The Veldt," originally published in *The Illustrated Man,* one of his many fine story collections, he returns to a favorite theme—the amorality of children.

Notes

flue	tube; pipe; enclosed passage as a means of conveyance
jumpers	sweaters
neurotic	too nervous
paprika	kind of red pepper
paranoia	type of mental disorder characterized by feelings of persecution
Pegasus	the flying horse in Greek mythology
Rima	the heroine of *Green Mansions,* a novel by W.H. Hudson
sonics	having to do with sound
spoor	tracks or trail of a wild animal
veldt	in South Africa, open country having grass and bushes but few trees
Tom Swift	the hero of a series of adventure novels for boys by Victor Appleby

THE WISH *(Page 116)*

Roald Dahl

Welsh-born American writer, Roald Dahl (1916-   ) is best known for unusual stories with surprise endings. In addition to being a prolific modern master of the macabre, he has found time to write children's books such as *Charlie and the Chocolate Factory* (1964) and *James and the Giant Peach* (1961). Some of his best stories have been collected in the popular *Tales of the Unexpected* (1979).

IMAGES *(page 124)*

Alice Munro

Born in Wingham, Ontario in 1931, Alice Munro graduated from the University of Western Ontario. She lived for a time in British Columbia and then returned to live in Ontario. A highly regarded short story writer and novelist, she has twice received the Governor-General's Award, in 1969 for her first volume of short stories, *Dance of the Happy Shades* (1968) and in 1978 for her book of short stories, *Who Do You Think You Are?*

Notes

diffidence	shyness
implacable	cannot be appeased or calmed
irascible	irritable
Orphan Annie	a cartoon character whose eyes were drawn as blank white ovals
resolutely	with determination
rigmarole	nonsense

A TELEVISION DRAMA *(page 137)*

Jane Rule

Born in Plainfield, New Jersey (1931), Jane Rule moved to Canada in 1956. While she has written many short stories and essays, she is recognized mainly for her work as a novelist. One of her novels, *The Young in One Another's Arms* (1977) was named the 1978 Best Novel of the Year by the Canadian Authors' Association. Her most recent book is *Inland Passage and Other Stories* (1985). She lives on Galiano Island, B.C.

Note

collage	a picture made by pasting onto a background material from different sources

THE SENTIMENTALISTS *(page 144)*

Morley Callaghan

Born in Toronto in 1903, Morley Callaghan graduated from the University of Toronto and began his writing career in 1923. After spending time in Paris and New York during the twenties and thirties, he settled again in Toronto. Author of numerous short stories and novels, he was awarded the 1952 Governor-General's Award for *Loved and the Lost* (1951) and has been nominated for the Nobel Prize. Callaghan's *That Summer in Paris* (1963) is one of the finest memoirs in Canadian literature. In 1975 Callaghan published *A Fine and Private Place* and in 1983, *A Time for Judas*. His children's story *Luke Baldwin's Vow* (1948) has been included in numerous children's anthologies.

Notes

cynically	doubting the sincerity of someone
incredulous	not believing
servile	grovelling, as a slave might

THE WITCH *(page 152)*

Shirley Jackson

A prolific short story writer and novelist, Shirley Jackson (1915-1965) was born in San Francisco. After graduating from university, she began working seriously at her career as a writer. A regular contributor to *The New Yorker*, she is best-known for two works: *The Haunting of Hill House* (1959) and "The Lottery" (1949).

DR. HEIDEGGER'S EXPERIMENT *(page 157)*

Nathaniel Hawthorne

Nathaniel Hawthorne (1804-1864) was born in Salem, Massachusetts. He attended college in Maine and later worked in a variety of careers, ranging from writing to working as a surveyor. Among his best-known works are *Twice-Told Tales* (1837; 1842) *The Scarlet Letter* (1850) and *The House of the Seven Gables* (1851).

Notes

damask	a reversible woven fabric
decrepit	old and feeble
deferential	respectful
dotage	a feeble mental condition associated with aging
festooned	hung in curves
folios, quartos, duodecimos	books of different sizes, ranging respectively from large to small
Hippocrates	a famous Greek physician
imbibe	to drink
imputed	attributed to
Ponce de Leon	a Spanish explorer (1460-1521)
quaffing	drinking deeply
suffusion	over-spread, as with color
tremulous	trembling
trolling	archaic term meaning to sing in full voice
venerable	respectable
veracious	true

THE OLD WOMAN (page 169)

Elizabeth Brewster

A teacher, librarian, short story writer, and prolific poet, Elizabeth
Brewster (1922-   ) makes her home in Saskatoon, Saskatchewan. Her
writing, which presents sensitive reflections on relationships and life
situations, is known to be positive and optimistic. A widely anthologized
poet, she has received, among other distinctions, the Canada Council
Senior Arts Award (1971-72) and the E.J. Pratt Gold Medal.

Notes

amethyst	a purple or violet quartz, used in jewellery
cenotaph	a monument to those killed in the war
conjectured	formed an opinion without sufficient evidence or proof; guessed
exasperated	extremely annoyed
forlornly	wretchedly, unhappily
tenure	permanent employment granted after a trial period

THE INTERLOPERS *(page 188)*

Saki

Saki (1870-1916) was the pen-name of Hector Hugh Munro, a famous Scottish short story writer who was born in Burma and educated in England. During his lifetime, he worked as a policeman for the Indian Imperial Police and as an editor for a London newspaper. He was killed in action in World War I, fighting in the British army. His stories are characterized by fantastic settings, unusual characters, and biting irony.

Notes

acquiesced	agreed to; submitted to
Carpathians	major forested mountain range in central and eastern Europe
draught	drink
interlopers	intruders
languor	weakness; weariness; sluggishness; feebleness
precipitous	steep
succor	relief; help in time of need, distress, or danger
wont	accustomed

PENNY IN THE DUST *(page 196)*

Ernest Buckler

Ernest Buckler (1908-1984) was born and raised in Dalhousie West, Nova Scotia. Later, he attended the University of Toronto and worked as an actuary for a Toronto insurance company before returning to his beloved Nova Scotia and a farm near Bridgetown where he did most of his writing.

Buckler wrote many fine stories and articles for such diverse magazines as *Maclean's, Chatelaine, Ladies' Home Journal, Esquire,* and *The Atlantic.* He won several awards and medals for his sensitive portrayals of human characters. His best-known work is the 1952 classic novel, *The Mountain and the Valley,* in which he wrote movingly of growing up in the Annapolis Valley.

Notes

Assyrian	a citizen of Assyria, an ancient country in the southwestern part of Asia
indulgently	kindly; not critically

FLIGHT (page 203)

Doris Lessing

Doris May Lessing (1919-) is a prominent British novelist, and short story and essay writer. Born in Iran to British parents, she grew up in the southern part of Zimbabwe, eventually moving to London in 1949. At different times, Lessing has been a nursemaid, shorthand-typist, telephone operator, left-wing political radical, and homemaker. Her interests range from female psychology to mysticism and to socialism. Her best-known work, an experimental novel called *The Golden Notebook,* (1962) is generally considered to be a landmark of the feminist movement.

Notes

dovecote	small house or shelter for pigeons or doves
frangipani	tropical red jasmine flower, known for its fragrance
incredulously	doubtfully; in disbelief
sardonic	bitter; sarcastic; scornful; mocking

BARNEY (page 211)

Will Stanton

Will Stanton (1918-1956) was an American writer of science fiction who during his lifetime was a farmer, construction worker, and house painter. He was a regular contributor of stories, poems, and articles to many publications in North America and abroad. For a decade, he wrote witty stories on familiar science-fiction themes for *FSF* (*Future Science Fiction*). "Barney" was first published in a 1951 issue of *FSF*.

Notes

coping	top layer of a brick or stone well or wall
facilitate	make easy; assist
glutamic acid	white crystalline amino acid obtained from proteins

THE CROOKED MAN *(page 215)*

Arthur Conan Doyle

Born in Edinburgh, Sir Arthur Conan Doyle (1859-1930) was an English physician, novelist and detective story writer. During his early career as a doctor he began to write while waiting for patients. In *A Study in Scarlet*, he introduced the reading public to his character Sherlock Holmes, who was to become the world's most famous fictional detective. The Holmes stories proved so successful, in fact, that Doyle quit his medical practice. At one point, he tried to "kill off" Holmes, but was forced to bring him back because of public protest.

In the Holmes stories, Doyle, himself an occasional consulting detective, originated the idea of the use of plaster of Paris for preserving delicate clues, the examination of dust from clothes for identification, the analysis of different qualities of various tobacco ashes, and the now universally-accepted science of deduction. The Chinese and Egyptian police have used these stories as their official training textbooks, and J. Edgar Hoover once declared that the F.B.I. followed Holmes's methods. "The Crooked Man" is one of 68 Holmes' cases and it originates from *The Memoirs of Sherlock Holmes*.

Notes

altercation	quarrel; angry dispute
cantonments	soldiers' quarters
conjecture	speculation; guessing
conjurer	magician or juggler
Crimea	region in southwest Russia where a war was fought by the English, French, and Turks against Russia (1854-1856)
fender	metal guard, frame, or screen in front of a fireplace
hansom	old-fashioned two-wheeled cab drawn by one horse
ichneumon	brownish mammal of Egypt resembling a weasel
meretricious	attractive in a showy way; alluring by false charms
mess	in armed services, place where soldiers eat
Mutiny	reference to a rebellion by native troops against the British in northern India in 1857
obscure	unclear; not obvious
obtrusively	intrusively; very noticeably

ostentatiously	in a showy fashion
Providence	God
puerile	childish
recriminations	counter-accusations
reproach	blame; disapproval
singular	peculiar; extraordinary; eccentric; strange
St. George	Christian martyr and patron saint of England
trepidation	great dread
vindictiveness	revengefulness; spite
wry	disgusted or grim-looking

A WAY OUT OF THE FOREST (page 234)

Maara Haas

Maara Haas, a graduate in journalism from the University of Berkeley, California, is best-known for her satirically humorous novel, *The Street Where I Live*. Other publications include poetry and prose in a variety of Canadian and American publications. Making her home in Manitoba, she spends five months of each year teaching writing in the Manitoba school system. Each fall she goes to Bermuda where she teaches creative writing courses. Often called "Manitoba's Story Lady," she has also been referred to as "Winnipeg's Mark Twain."

Notes

cache	hidden supply
cherubs	child-angels
Grand Marais	small resort town near Grand Beach, Manitoba
New Monia	pneumonia; a disease in which the lungs get inflamed (a disease more likely to afflict the poverty-stricken)
R 177599	an Indian treaty number issued to the father by the government
suet	hard fat about the kidneys and loins of sheep or cattle

Glossary of Terms

allusion

An allusion is a direct or indirect reference to a familiar figure, place, or event from history, literature, mythology, or from the Bible. Most allusions expand on or develop a significant idea, impression, or mood.

At the end of "The Crooked Man," Holmes explains that when Mrs. Barclay exclaimed the name "David," she was making an allusion to a story in the Old Testament. In the story, King David sent out his captain Uriah into the most dangerous part of the battle, where he was slain. David did this in order to gain Uriah's wife, Bathsheba, whom he coveted. This story parallels the incidents of the Indian subplot-love triangle in the Doyle story and emphasizes the note of betrayal.

antagonist

The antagonist is the major character or force that opposes the protagonist. The antagonist in "The Sea Devil" is the ray, and the antagonists in "The Veldt" are Peter and Wendy.

antecedent action

This is significant action that has taken place before the story begins. Early in "The Father," the protagonist recalls a significant trip to the boy's school which had contributed to his and his father's drifting apart. In the second paragraph of "The Interlopers," the reader is given background to the feud.

anticlimax

An event or conclusion that is an abrupt shift from the important to the comical or trivial is an anticlimax. The concluding events in "The Veldt" and the September 11th entry in "Barney" are examples of anticlimax.

atmosphere (or mood)
The atmosphere or mood is the prevailing feeling that is created in a story. The atmosphere usually sets up the reader's expectations about the ending or outcome of the plot. Atmosphere is usually created through the dialogue and the imagery. The atmosphere of "Wish You Were Here" is tense and menacing. Like Mrs. Graham, the reader wants to know the identity of Mr. Gnome and his motivation for sending the odd postcards.

character
This is a term used to describe 1) the fictional persons who carry out the action of a story, and 2) the moral and dispositional qualities of a fictional person in a story. The latter is generally revealed through dialogue, action, and description. Characters themselves may be classified as: *round* or *flat*, *realistic* or *stereotyped*, *static* or *dynamic*. (See definitions for these words in this Glossary.)

characterization
Characterization is a method of presenting the special qualities or features of a character in a literary work. Basically, the short story will either reveal character directly (through the author's comments) or indirectly (through the character's speech, thoughts, and actions).

The character of Mary McQuade in "Images" is revealed through what she says about herself, what the young narrator says about her, and through the dinner-table dialogue and actions of both Mary and the narrator's father.

character sketch
A character sketch is a description of a character's moral and dispositional qualities using nouns, adjectives, and specific examples and quotations from the story. It does not normally describe the character's physical appearance and dress.

A portion of a character sketch on Mary McQuade in "Images" might read as follows:

Mary McQuade is an imposing character in Alice Munro's "Images." She terrifies the narrator who regards her as "big and gloomy as an iceberg." At the same time, she is also described as a chronic complainer in the episodes when she hangs the wash and when she chides the narrator for disturbing her sick mother.

climax
From the reader's perspective, the climax is the highest point of emotional intensity in a story. It usually marks the turning point in the protagonist's fortunes and the major crisis in the story.

The climax of "Dr. Heidegger's Experiment" occurs when the doctor's rejuvenated friends knock over the vase of precious water from the Fountain of Youth. The climax of "The Sentimentalists" occurs when Malone reveals to the shoplifter his reasons for preventing her arrest.

complicating incident (or complication)

The incident that initiates a conflict is the complicating incident. In "The Friday Everything Changed," the complicating incident occurs when Alma Niles asks Miss Ralston why the girls can't carry the water bucket. The complication in "The Wish" arises when the young boy sets out to cross the large carpet.

confidant (or confidante)

A confidant/confidante is a trusted friend of the protagonist who shares his or her thoughts, feelings, and intentions. Dr. Watson in "The Crooked Man" is an example of a confidant. Florrie in "The Old Woman" finds herself unwillingly cast in the role of confidante to her senile neighbour, Mrs. Cornish.

conflict

A conflict is a struggle between opposing characters or forces, usually between the protagonist and someone or something else. All conflicts are either external (physical) or internal (emotional, moral, psychological). There are three main conflicts discussed below:

1) *Conflict between a character and his or her environment* (whether this be nature, society, or circumstance).

In "A Television Drama," Carolee Mitchell's quiet suburban life is disrupted by the unexpected intrusion of violence and the resultant media coverage. In "A Mountain Journey," Dave Conroy battles the elements to reach his destination.

2) *Conflict between two characters* This struggle may be physical, emotional, moral, or psychological.

In "The Old Woman," Florrie Middleton eventually ends up avoiding contact with Mrs. Cornish, an elderly neighbor who desperately want her friendship. In "The Whale," village fishermen mock Ambroise Bourdages who earnestly claims to have caught a whale with a herring-baited rope-hook.

3) *Conflict within a character* The character, in this case, experiences a conflict in emotion or thought.

In "Flight," the old man struggles with his desire to keep and to part with his favorite bird and his youngest granddaughter. In "Who Said We All Have to Talk Alike", the "homebody" Neffie becomes restless with the urge to go out and see more of the world.

contrast (or juxtaposition)

Contrast refers to the overlap or mixing of situations, characters, settings, moods, or points of view in order to clarify meaning, purpose, or character, or to heighten certain moods, especially humor, horror, and suspense.

In "A Mountain Journey," there is a contrast between Dave Conroy's desire to reach safety and his desire for rest from travelling. In "The Sentimentalists," the bored cynicism of Fred Webster is contrasted to the surprising emotional involvement of his friend Jack Malone in the plight of the shoplifter.

crisis

The crisis is a moment of intense conflict leading up the the climax.

A crisis occurs early in "The Veldt" when Lydia and George narrowly escape an attack by the lions in their children's nursery. Another crisis can be found in "The Sentimentalists" when Malone overcomes his disgust and unexpectedly steers the shoplifter out of the clutches of the store detective.

dénouement (or resolution)

Dénouement (pronounced day-NEW-mahn) is a French term to describe the "unknotting" of plot or conflict following a climax. The final episode of "The Crooked Man", in which Holmes enlightens Watson about the remaining unexplained facts of the Barclay case, is a dénouement.

dialect

Dialect is a form of speech characteristic of a particular geographic region, social class, or a people.

In "The Interlopers," Znaeym and Von Gradwitz use expressions such as "forest-thief", "game-snatcher" which suggest that they are east Europeans. In "Alicia," the story's translator retains certain French names, words, and expressions such as "Maman," and "Petite Misère," to remind us of the ethnic background of the characters and setting.

dialogue

A conversation including two or more characters in a story is a dialogue. Dialogue is often used to reveal character and conflict.

diction

Diction is a style of speaking or writing resulting from a deliberate choice and arrangement of words in a story. Each writer uses diction appropriate to his or her purpose, subject, story type, characters, and style.

In "Dr. Heidegger's Experiment," Hawthorne uses a nineteenth-century style of diction, appropriate for his time, but one which may send modern readers to their dictionaries to find the meanings of such old-fashioned words as "mendicant" and "damask." In "Barney," Will Stanton uses first-person pronouns and such words as "guinea pig" and "experiments" to create the feeling of a scientist's journal.

dilemma
A dilemma is a situation in which a character must make a difficult choice between two disagreeable, undesirable, or unfavorable alternatives. Dilemma is one method by which an author can generate suspense in a story.

In "The Sea Devil," immediately before the climax, the man faces a dilemma: "All he knew was that in five seconds or less he would be dragged into the stake and cut to ribbons if he tried to hold on; or drowned if he didn't."

dynamic character
A character, often the protagonist, who undergoes a significant, lasting change, usually in his or her outlook on life, is a dynamic character.

In "The Carved Table," Karen sees her new family through the eyes of her first husband and this results in a major change in her attitude toward her new husband and his family. Carolee Mitchell in "A Television Drama" is another character who is affected permanently as a result of violence in her neighborhood.

epiphany
An epiphany is a moment of significant realization which happens to the main character, usually at the end of a story.

One character who has an epiphany is John Purcell in "The Father," when he realizes that he is to blame for the major rift between himself and his son. At the conclusion of "The Carved Table," Karen realizes she is different from her new husband and his family, that she is her own agent, and must start to make decisions for herself.

episode
A episode is an incident or a single set of events within the main plot of the story.

Ambroise's trip with Clovis in "The Whale" is an example of an episode. Another example occurs in "The Old Woman" when Florrie and her boyfriend Reg discuss ways of contacting Mrs. Cornish's relatives.

escapist fiction
This refers to a type of fiction which is designed to help the reader "escape" the daily cares and problems of reality. Escapist fiction has lively,

melodramatic plots and stereotyped or flat characters, and requires limited involvement on the part of the reader. Most commercial science fiction, westerns, and romances would fall into the category of escapist fiction.

"Barney," and "A Mountain Journey," are examples of escapist fiction because of their emphasis on plot and physical action, their lack of complex characterizations, and absence of high or serious purpose.

exposition
Exposition is background information provided by the author to further the plot, conflict, setting, and characterization.

In the beginning of "Penny in the Dust," the narrator and his sister recall a childhood event in which a new penny was believed lost and became the object of an intensive search. "Wish You Were Here" begins with background on Dorothy's initial fascination with and subsequent purchase of the garden gnome.

falling action
The part of a story immediately following a climax and lasting until the end of the story is called the falling action.

The falling action of "The Witch" occurs after the mother chases the strange man from the railway coach. "The Interlopers" ends with a climax and so it has no falling action.

fantasy
A fantasy is a highly exaggerated or improbable story. As a rule, events, characters, and settings in a fantasy would not be possible or found in real life.

"The Wish," "Barney," and "The Veldt" are all examples of fantasy.

fiction
Fiction is any narrative which is imagined and invented rather than historically or factually true. It includes novels as well as short stories.

flashback
A flashback is a plot device which shifts the story from the present to the past, usually done in order to illustrate an important point or to reveal a change in character.

Stories with flashbacks include "Penny in the Dust" and "Alicia."

flat character
A limited character, usually a minor character who has only one apparent quality, is a flat character.

The mother-in-law in "The Carved Table," and Fred Webster in "The Sentimentalists" are flat characters.

foil

A foil is a character whose behavior, attitudes, and opinions are in contrast to those of the protagonist. He/she helps the reader to understand better the character of the protagonist. Florrie Middleton and Mrs. Cornish are foils in "The Old Woman."

foreshadowing

This device gives a hint of what is to happen later in the story. It prepares the reader for the climax, the resolution, and for changes, or lack of changes, in character attitude.

In "Wish You Were Here," the postman's involvement in the deadly prank is foreshadowed by Norman's initial interest in the gnome and his conversation with Dorothy whenever she receives postcards from Mr. Gnome.

form

Form is a general term referring to the way in which a story is put together, its "shape" or structure. Form is sometimes called the "how" of a story and includes both technique and author's style.

"Barney" follows the forms of the journal and the science fiction story while "The Crooked Man" follows the conventions of the mystery story. "A Way Out of the Forest," makes strong use of narrative exposition, description, and dialogue to underscore the poverty of the children's family.

goal

This is the aim of the protagonist. Many protagonists have aims which they strive to accomplish. The desire to achieve a goal often creates conflict, and failure or success in achieving a goal is frequently apparent in the climax of a story.

The goal of the boy in "The Wish" is to safely cross the carpet, avoiding imaginary pitfalls. The goal of the protagonist in "The Father"—to become closer to his son—is not accomplished because of his embarrassing drunken behavior at the Boy Scout banquet.

hero (or heroine)

This is the principal male or female character in a story who possesses heroic qualities or virtues. The terms "hero" and "heroine" are not interchangeable with the more general term "protagonist."

Sherlock Holmes is the hero in "The Crooked Man" by virtue of his cleverness in solving the baffling death of Colonel Barclay. In "The Friday Everything Changed," Miss Ralson achieves the status of a heroine in the eyes of her female students when she hits an impressive home run.

humor
Writing which is intended to amuse the reader or to provoke laughter is humor.

The writer's purpose in "The Whale" is to entertain and amuse the reader with his tall-tale form and his ironic surprise ending for the romantic subplot.

images
Images are concrete details and figures of speech that help the reader to form vivid sense impressions of what is being described.

The young narrator of "Images" describes Mary McQuade through these images: ". . . she turned out to be freckled all over, everywhere you could see, as if she was sprinkled with oatmeal, and she had a crown of frizzy, glinting, naturally brass-colored hair."

indeterminate ending
A story ending in which there is no clear outcome or result is called an indeterminate ending.

Although Rouga and Arnie are leaving home in "A Way Out of the Forest," it is not clear what will ultimately happen to them.

interpretive fiction
This refers to stories which have meaningful, usually realistic plots, conflicts, settings, and characters. Interpretive fiction is usually serious in tone and is designed to "interpret" or make the reader more aware of, some aspect of reality or human nature. It is instructive, unlike escapist fiction, which is designed chiefly for entertainment. Most of the stories in this book are examples of interpretive fiction.

irony
Irony is a literary device which reveals concealed or contradictory meaning(s). Three common forms of irony are:

1) *Verbal irony*, which occurs when a contrast is evident between what a character says and what that character actually means.

In "Images," the father is teasing Mary McQuade about the hermit Joe when he says, "We found the one for you today."

2) *Dramatic irony*, which occurs when the author shares with the reader information not known by a character. As a result, the reader becomes aware that a character's actions may be inappropriate for the actual circumstances, that what is to come is the reverse of what a character expects, or that a character has unknowingly made a comment which anticipates the outcome.

An example of dramatic irony occurs in "Barney" when the narrator says that he should make himself a sandwich as he is likely to be down in the well for a long time.

3) *Situational irony*, (or irony of situation) which occurs when a set of circumstances turn out differently from what was expected or considered appropriate.

In "The Parsley Garden," Al surprises his mother by refusing a job and money earned from working at the store.

juxtaposition
See *contrast*.

local color
Local color is the use of specific regional detail in order to increase atmosphere or reader interest and a sense of setting. Local color includes descriptions of locale, dress, and customs as well as dialect and ways of thinking and feeling characteristic of people in that region.

"A Mountain Journey" gives the reader a strong sense of a Rocky Mountain setting in winter through its references to treeless summits, mountain passes, spruce trees, alplands, snowbanks, ice and cabins. Real and fictional placenames such as Jasper, Hoodoo Creek, the Jackpine, Snake Indian River, Moose River, and Terrace Creek also help to create the illusion of a mountain setting.

mood
See *atmosphere*.

moral
The implied or stated lesson of a story is called the moral. Viewed in isolation, a moral is a relatively unimportant part of a story and should not be confused with a more significant fictional element—*Theme*.

Sometimes, morals are directly stated, as in the case of Aesop's Fables. At the end of "The Sea Devil," the fisherman has learned his lesson. As he says, "He knew he would do no more casting alone at night. Not in the dark of the moon. No, not he." The unstated moral of "Flight" would be that "letting go" of loved ones is a difficult, but necessary, phase of life.

motivation
This is what causes a character to do what he or she does. Circumstance and temperament usually determine the actions of a character. Characters must have sufficient and plausible motivation in order for a reader to find a story realistic or effective.

In "Penny in the Dust," Peter's motivation for hiding in the house is his personal disappointment in losing the penny that he had imagined as a stepping stone to a happier future for his father and himself. In "The Sentimentalists," Malone's instinct to protect the shoplifter causes him to intervene unexpectedly on her behalf.

mystery story (or whodunit)

This is a suspense story such as "The Crooked Man" which contains a crime and, finally, a solution by a detective. Good mysteries contain intriguing plots and "red herrings" (false clues or suspects).

The typical pattern of the mystery story is as follows:
1) discovery of the crime
2) collection of evidence
3) misdirected suspicion
4) movement of action toward a second crime
5) surprise solution
6) explanation and dénouement ("unknotting")

narrative

This is another word for story. Narratives have the following elements: plot, conflict, characters, setting, point of view, and theme. Narratives may be fictional or non-fictional, and include novels and (auto)biographies as well as short stories and anecdotes.

plot

The storyline or organization of incidents in a story is called the plot. It consists of episodes and conflict. Plots usually have rising and falling action, a climax, and a resolution.

point of view

The point of view is the perspective from which a story is seen or told. Importantly, it establishes the relationships of author, reader, and protagonist. The three most common points of view are:

1) *First-person narrative*, which features the protagonist telling his or her own story directly to the reader using the first person ("*I*"). This point of view tells us what the main character thinks and feels from a vantage point "inside" the story and the protagonist.

"Penny in the Dust" and "Alicia," are examples of first-person narratives.

2) *Limited omniscient narrative* (*Third-person narrative*) which refers to the main character as "he" or "she," and which shows us only what one character thinks and feels, but from the perspective of someone "outside" the story.

"Flight," "The Father," and "A Way Out of the Forest" are all examples of limited omniscient narratives.

3) *Omniscient narrative* which reveals the minds of several or all characters, knowing and telling all from an all-seeing, God-like perspective "outside" the story.

"The Whale" and "Dr. Heidegger's Experiment" are omniscient narratives.

predicament
This is a position or situation that is difficult to get out of or that presents a problem difficult to solve. Predicaments should not be confused with dilemmas.

In "Alicia," the parents experience a predicament when they are unsure of what to do about Alicia. Another predicament occurs in "The Friday Everything Changed" when the girls of the school, under pressure from the boys, have mixed feelings about whether or not the water-carrying responsibility is worth all the harrassment they are subjected to.

prose
Ordinary language or literary expression not marked by rhythm or rhyme is called prose. This type of language is used in short stories, essays, and modern plays.

protagonist
The protagonist is the main character of a story. While some protagonists may be heroes or heroines, more typically they are like people we meet in real life: they have a mixture of characteristics, some of which may be weaknesses.

The protagonists in "Penny in the Dust," "Flight," and "Who Said We All Have to Talk Alike" are, respectively, Peter, Grandad, and Neffie.

purpose
The story's purpose is the main effect a story is intended to achieve. Authors usually have a specific intention, such as to entertain, enlighten, or to demonstrate something about life or human nature. Purpose may include theme, but should not simply be equated to the story's main idea. Stories often have more than one purpose.

The main purpose of "Dr. Heidegger's Experiment" is to show that, if given a second chance, people would likely make the same mistakes again. Other purposes of Hawthorne's story would be:
1) to tell an intriguing tale about the elusive Fountain of Youth,
2) to show how human beings delude themselves to achieve a desired goal,
3) to reveal the wistfulness of the elderly, and
4) to suggest how tampering with science and the unknown can lead to dire consequences.

realism
This refers to any subject matter or techniques that create a "true-to-life" impression on the reader. Writers of realism record life "as it is" and allow

stories "to tell themselves". Realism can also refer to stories which are about simple, everyday people.

The term "realism" could be applied to the portrayal of the father-son conflict in "The Father," the movie-like atmosphere of "A Television Drama," and the shifting points of view in "The Old Woman."

resolution
See *dénouement*.

rising action
The rising action consists of the events preceding the climax. During this stage of the story, background information is given, conflicts are introduced, and suspense is built up. There may even be moments of crisis. Because it accomplishes so much, the rising action is always longer than the falling action of a story.

In "A Mountain Journey," all events up to the second time Conroy rests would be considered rising action. In "The Sea Devil," the rising action ends when the man breaks the rope connecting him to the ray.

romance
A romance is an entertaining story which contains one or more of the following elements: fantasy, improbability, extravagance, naiveté, love, adventure, and myth.

One example of a romance is "The Whale," a tall tale which contains love, adventure, and naiveté. Other stories having elements found in romance include: "Images," "The Sea Devil," "The Veldt," "The Witch," and "A Way Out of the Forest".

round character
A round character is a realistic character having several sides to his/her nature.

The mailman in "Wish You Were Here" and Florrie Middleton and Mrs. Cornish in "The Old Woman" are examples of round characters.

satire
Satire is the ridicule of an idea, person, or type, sometimes in order to provoke change. Satire usually mocks human vices or foibles.

"The Witch" satirizes the conventional "bribery" of young children by well-meaning parents through its lollipop symbol.

science fiction
Science fiction is imaginative writing which speculates about the effect of technology, science, and the future on human beings. Some science fiction

is light and intended mostly as escapist entertainment, while another type of science fiction is more thoughtful, serious-minded, and interpretive in its purpose.

Both "Barney" and "The Veldt" deal with improbable events that depend on science for their complications and conflicts. In the former, a rat has gained the intelligence to read, write, and outwit the scientist-narrator. In the latter, a simulated environment eventually leads to the murder of both parents.

setting

The setting is the time and place of a story.

"The Friday Everything Changed" is set in the Maritimes in the years following World War II. Because of the Chicago and Viet Nam references, "The Carved Table" would likely be set in America of the late 1970s.

short story

A brief, fictional prose narrative having one main character, a single plot, a limited number of settings, and one main single effect constitutes a short story.

Edgar Allan Poe, one of the first significant theorists and practitioners of short story writing, said that short stories:

1) can be read in one sitting, and derive their power from the fact that the writer has to select details for economy and emphasis;
2) have a single "effect" or purpose and are constructed so that every sentence from the first to the last one supports that "effect";
3) leave the reader with a feeling of satisfaction and "finality," desiring no further completion or alternate ending, and
4) have their basis in truth (life-likeness).

static character

A static character is one who does not change in the course of a story. Often, protagonists who are static characters fail to achieve their goals or are defeated by their unwillingness to change or adapt.

Characters who do not change in the course of their stories include Mary McQuade in "Images," the doctor's friends in "Dr. Heidegger's Experiment," and Sherlock Holmes and Dr. Watson in "The Crooked Man."

stereotype

A stereotype is any fixed pattern based on plot or character. Stereotyped plots usually fall into the realm of escapist fiction. Stereotyped characters are familiar figures in fiction such as the "hard-boiled" private investigator, the absent-minded professor, the "stiff upper lip" officer, and the imperiled heroine from Victorian melodrama.

The plot of "A Mountain Journey" is a variation of the pattern in which a man is defeated by his carelessness and by nature. This pattern has been explored before in other stories such as Jack London's "To Build a Fire". Sherlock Holmes has spawned many methodical detectives who are stereotyped variations of his character.

stream-of-consciousness
A modern technique for depicting thoughts and feelings of a character in an apparently natural way without logic or interruption is the stream-of-consciousness technique. The author using stream-of-consciousness deliberately includes important details relevant to plot, character, and theme in the stream-of-consciousness.

Portions of "The Old Woman" are written in a stream-of-consciousness style, e.g., "Had Perce and Ida taken her to live with them? Probably not. After all, would she?"

style
Style is the individual manner in which an author expresses his or her thoughts and feelings. In fiction, style is basically determined by such grammatical and sensory aspects as diction, sentences, and images.

"The Friday Everything Changed" is written in a light, conversational and anecdotal style which complements the viewpoint of the young narrator. The vigorous, dynamic style of "The Sea Devil" stems from its strong, forceful nouns, adjectives, and verbs.

subplot
A subplot is a minor storyline, secondary to the main plot. Subplots may be related or unrelated to the main action, but may also be a reflection or variation of the main plot.

In "The Crooked Man," there is an important subplot set in India involving Colonel Barclay, his wife, and Henry Wood. In "Images," there is a subplot involving the narrator's and her father's relationships with Mary McQuade.

surprise ending
The sudden twist in the direction of a story, producing a conclusion which surprises the reader and often the story's characters as well, is called a surprise ending.

One example of the surprise ending occurs in "A Way Out of the Forest" when Arnie and Rouga's make-believe journey becomes a real one to the City. Another surprise ending occurs in "The Interlopers" when the two noblemen discover that their would-be rescuers are actually wolves.

suspense

Suspense is the feeling of anxiety and uncertainty experienced by the reader about the outcome of events or the protagonist's destiny.

Stories which build suspense include "The Friday Everything Changed," "Wish You Were Here," "The Veldt," and "A Television Drama."

symbol

A symbol is something that stands for or represents something else. Characters, objects, events, and settings can all be symbolic.

A symbolic character is the protagonist in "The Sea Devil," who represents civilized man engaged in a struggle against the ray, which, in turn, represents the primitive, destructive aspects of nature. Another symbol is the penny in "Penny in the Dust." On one level, to the boy, the penny represents his romantic desire for material goods for his father. On another level, to the father, the penny represents his recognition and appreciation of his son's love for him as well as his own love for his son.

tale

A tale is a story which is loosely plotted, often told by a narrator, and has limited character development. Stories which are exotic, bizarre, or adventurous are called tales.

Two tales which are loosely plotted with little character development are "The Witch" and "The Whale." Because of its bizarre events, "Dr. Heidegger's Experiment" could also be classified as a tale.

theme

The theme is the central idea of a story, usually implied rather than directly stated. Theme should not be confused with either moral or plot.

In "The Witch," the theme is that despite society's efforts to instill acceptable behaviour in us, we still have a darker aggressive nature that emerges occasionally. In "The Old Woman," we see that the problems associated with aging could become part of our experience. One theme is that changes in attitude can sometimes occur too late to undo the damages done by irrational hatred or jealousy.

universality

This is a term that means that a story is broad enough to be applied to most people at any time or place. Stories having universality reveal human nature or common truths of experience. Universality is also taken by some critics to be a criterion for measuring the worth or success of a story.

Stories in this book with important human concerns or moral truths include "Dr. Heidegger's Experiment" and "Flight." The fact that these stories are universal in their impact and significance makes them stand out over "lighter" stories such as "Barney."

verisimilitude

Verisimilitude is a life-like quality possessed by a story as revealed through its plot, setting, conflict, and characterization.

vicarious experience

The feeling a reader has when emotionally or mentally involved in a story is a vicarious experience. He or she imaginatively experiences and shares some of the same things as the characters in the story.

Obviously, the effect of powerful stories such as "The Wish" and "The Sea Devil" depends upon how much the reader identifies with the protagonist.

whodunit

See *mystery story*.

PERMISSION CREDITS

PHOTO CREDITS